J Ainslie
1886

5d

THE WORKS

OF

W. M. THACKERAY

THE WORKS

OF

WILLIAM MAKEPEACE THACKERAY

IN TWENTY-SIX VOLUMES.

VOLUME XXI.

BALLADS

AND

THE ROSE AND THE RING

LONDON

SMITH, ELDER, & CO., 15 WATERLOO PLACE

1879

BALLADS

THE ROSE AND THE RING

BY

WILLIAM MAKEPEACE THACKERAY

WITH ILLUSTRATIONS BY
THE AUTHOR, MRS BUTLER (MISS ELIZABETH THOMPSON),
GEORGE DU MAURIER, JOHN COLLIER, H. FURNISS, G. G. KILBURNE
M. FITZGERALD, AND J. P. ATKINSON

LONDON
SMITH, ELDER, & CO., 15 WATERLOO PLACE
1879

ADVERTISEMENT

———◆◇◆———

This Edition of Mr. Thackeray's 'Ballads' will be found to include all the verses that are scattered throughout the Author's various writings

CONTENTS.

BALLADS.

LOVE-SONGS MADE EASY.

FIVE GERMAN DITTIES.

FOUR IMITATIONS OF BÉRANGER.

IMITATION OF HORACE.

OLD FRIENDS WITH NEW FACES.

LYRA HIBERNICA.

THE BALLADS OF POLICEMAN X.

THE ROSE AND THE RING.

LIST OF ILLUSTRATIONS.

———◆———

THE ROSE AND THE RING.

BALLADS

BALLADS.

THE CHRONICLE OF THE DRUM.

PART I.

AT Paris, hard by the Maine barriers,
　　Whoever will choose to repair,
Midst a dozen of wooden-legged warriors
　　May haply fall in with old Pierre.
On the sunshiny bench of a tavern
　　He sits and he prates of old wars,
And moistens his pipe of tobacco
　　With a drink that is named after Mars.

The beer makes his tongue run the quicker,
   And as long as his tap never fails,
Thus over his favourite liquor
   Old Peter will tell his old tales.
Says he, " In my life's ninety summers
   Strange changes and chances I've seen,—
So here's to all gentlemen drummers
   That ever have thumped on a skin.

" Brought up in the art military
   For four generations we are ;
My ancestors drumm'd for King Harry,
   The Huguenot lad of Navarre.
And as each man in life has his station
   According as Fortune may fix,
While Condé was waving the bâton,
   My grandsire was trolling the sticks.

" Ah ! those were the days for commanders !
   What glories my grandfather won,
Ere bigots, and lackeys, and panders
   The fortunes of France had undone !
In Germany, Flanders, and Holland,—
   What foeman resisted us then ?
No ; my grandsire was ever victorious,
   My grandsire and Monsieur Turenne.

" He died : and our noble battalions
   The jade fickle Fortune forsook ;
And at Blenheim, in spite of our valiance,
   The victory lay with Malbrook.
The news it was brought to King Louis ;
   Corbleu ! how his Majesty swore
When he heard they had taken my grandsire :
   And twelve thousand gentlemen more.

" At Namur, Ramillies, and Malplaquet
   Were we posted, on plain or in trench :
Malbrook only need to attack it
   And away from him scamper'd we French.

Cheer up ! 'tis no use to be glum, boys,—
'Tis written, since fighting begun,
That sometimes we fight and we conquer,
And sometimes we fight and we run.

" To fight and to run was our fate :
Our fortune and fame had departed.
And so perish'd Louis the Great,—
Old, lonely, and half broken-hearted.
His coffin they pelted with mud,
His body they tried to lay hands on ;
And so having buried King Louis
They loyally served his great-grandson.

" God save the beloved King Louis !
(For so he was nicknamed by some,)
And now came my father to do his
King's orders and beat on the drum.
My grandsire was dead, but his bones
Must have shaken, I'm certain, for joy,
To hear daddy drumming the English
From the meadows of famed Fontenoy.

" So well did he drum in that battle
That the enemy show'd us their backs ;
Corbleu ! it was pleasant to rattle
The sticks and to follow old Saxe !
We next had Soubise as a leader,
And as luck hath its changes and fits,
At Rosbach, in spite of dad's drumming,
'Tis said we were beaten by Fritz.

" And now daddy cross'd the Atlantic,
To drum for Montcalm and his men ;
Morbleu ! but it makes a man frantic
To think we were beaten again !
My daddy he cross'd the wide ocean,
My mother brought me on her neck,
And we came in the year fifty-seven
To guard the good town of Quebec.

" In the year fifty-nine came the Britons,—
  Full well I remember the day,—
They knocked at our gates for admittance,
  Their vessels were moor'd in our bay.
Says our general, ' Drive me yon red-coats
  Away to the sea whence they come !'
So we march'd against Wolfe and his bull-dogs,
  We marched at the sound of the drum.

" I think I can see my poor mammy
  With me in her hand as she waits,
And our regiment, slowly retreating,
  Pours back through the citadel gates.
Dear mammy she looks in their faces,
  And asks if her husband is come ?
—He is lying all cold on the glacis,
  And will never more beat on the drum.

" Come, drink, 'tis no use to be glum, boys !
  He died like a soldier in glory ;
Here's a glass to the health of all drum-boys,
  And now I'll commence my own story.
Once more did we cross the salt ocean,
  We came in the year eighty-one ;
And the wrongs of my father the drummer
  Were avenged by the drummer his son.

" In Chesapeak Bay we were landed.
  In vain strove the British to pass :
Rochambeau our armies commanded,
  Our ships they were led by De Grasse.
Morbleu ! how I rattled the drumsticks
  The day we march'd into Yorktown ;
Ten thousand of beef-eating British
  Their weapons we caused to lay down.

" Then homewards returning victorious,
  In peace to our country we came,
And were thanked for our glorious actions
  By Louis, Sixteenth of the name.

What drummer on earth could be prouder
  Than I, while I drumm'd at Versailles
To the lovely court ladies in powder,
  And lappets, and long satin-tails?

" The princes that day pass'd before us,
  Our countrymen's glory and hope ;
Monsieur, who was learned in Horace,
  D'Artois, who could dance the tight-rope.
One night we kept guard for the Queen
  At her Majesty's opera-box,
While the King, that majestical monarch,
  Sat filing at home at his locks.

" Yes, I drumm'd for the fair Antoinette,
  And so smiling she look'd and so tender,
That our officers, privates, and drummers,
  All vow'd they would die to defend her.
But she cared not for us honest fellows,
  Who fought and who bled in her wars,
She sneer'd at our gallant Rochambeau,
  And turned Lafayette out of doors.

" Ventrebleu ! then I swore a great oath,
  No more to such tyrants to kneel ;
And so, just to keep up my drumming,
  One day I drumm'd down the Bastille.
Ho, landlord ! a stoup of fresh wine.
  Come, comrades, a bumper we'll try,
And drink to the year eighty-nine
  And the glorious fourth of July !

" Then bravely our cannon it thunder'd
  As onwards our patriots bore.
Our enemies were but a hundred,
  And we twenty thousand or more.
They carried the news to King Louis.
  He heard it as calm as you please,
And, like a majestical monarch,
  Kept filing his locks and his keys.

" We show'd our republican courage,
    We storm'd and we broke the great gate in,
And we murder'd the insolent governor
    For daring to keep us a-waiting.
Lambesc and his squadrons stood by :
    They never stirr'd finger or thumb.
The saucy aristocrats trembled
    As they heard the republican drum.

" Hurrah ! what a storm was a-brewing !
    The day of our vengeance was come !
Through scenes of what carnage and ruin
    Did I beat on the patriot drum !
Let's drink to the famed tenth of August :
    At midnight I beat the tattoo,
And woke up the pikemen of Paris
    To follow the bold Barbaroux.

" With pikes, and with shouts, and with torches
    March'd onwards our dusty battalions,
And we girt the tall castle of Louis,
    A million of tatterdemalions !
We storm'd the fair gardens where tower'd
    The walls of his heritage splendid.
Ah, shame on him, craven and coward,
    That had not the heart to defend it !

" With the crown of his sires on his head,
    His nobles and knights by his side,
At the foot of his ancestors' palace
    'Twere easy, methinks, to have died.
But no : when we burst through his barriers,
    Mid heaps of the dying and dead,
In vain through the chambers we sought him—
    He had turn'd like a craven and fled.

*   *   *   *

" You all know the Place de la Concorde ?
    'Tis hard by the Tuileries wall.
Mid terraces, fountains, and statues,
    There rises an obelisk tall.

There rises an obelisk tall,
　　All garnish'd and gilded the base is :
'Tis surely the gayest of all
　　Our beautiful city's gay places.

" Around it are gardens and flowers,
　　And the Cities of France on their thrones,
Each crown'd with his circlet of flowers
　　Sits watching this biggest of stones !
I love to go sit in the sun there,
　　The flowers and fountains to see,
And to think of the deeds that were done there
　　In the glorious year ninety-three.

" 'Twas here stood the Altar of Freedom ;
　　And though neither marble nor gilding
Was used in those days to adorn
　　Our simple republican building,
Corbleu ! but the MÈRE GUILLOTINE
　　Cared little for splendour or show,
So you gave her an axe and a beam,
　　And a plank and a basket or so.

" Awful, and proud, and erect,
　　Here sat our republican goddess.
Each morning her table we deck'd
　　With dainty aristocrats' bodies.
The people each day flocked around
　　As she sat at her meat and her wine :
'Twas always the use of our nation
　　To witness the sovereign dine.

" Young virgins with fair golden tresses,
　　Old silver-hair'd prelates and priests,
Dukes, marquises, barons, princesses,
　　Were splendidly served at her feasts.
Ventrebleu ! but we pamper'd our ogress
　　With the best that our nation could bring,
And dainty she grew in her progress,
　　And called for the head of a King !

"She called for the blood of our King,
      And straight from his prison we drew him ;
And to her with shouting we led him,
      And took him, and bound him, and slew him.
' The monarchs of Europe against me
      Have plotted a godless alliance :
I'll fling them the head of King Louis,'
      She said, ' as my gage of defiance.'

"I see him as now, for a moment,
      Away from his gaolers he broke ;
And stood at the foot of the scaffold,
      And linger'd, and fain would have spoke.
' Ho, drummer ! quick, silence yon Capet,'
      Says Santerre, ' with a beat of your drum.'
Lustily then did I tap it,
      And the son of Saint Louis was dumb.

       *   *   *   *

PART II.

"THE glorious days of September
　　Saw many aristocrats fall ;
'Twas then that our pikes drank the blood
　　In the beautiful breast of Lamballe.
Pardi, 'twas a beautiful lady !
　　I seldom have look'd on her like ;
And I drumm'd for a gallant procession,
　　That marched with her head on a pike.

"Let's show the pale head to the Queen,
　　We said—she'll remember it well.
She looked from the bars of her prison,
　　And shriek'd as she saw it, and fell.

We set up a shout at her screaming,
　　We laugh'd at the fright she had shown
At the sight of the head of her minion—
　　How she'd tremble to part with her own!

"We had taken the head of King Capet,
　　We called for the blood of his wife;
Undaunted she came to the scaffold,
　　And bared her fair neck to the knife.
As she felt the foul fingers that touch'd her,
　　She shrank, but she deigned not to speak:
She look'd with a royal disdain,
　　And died with a blush on her cheek!

"'Twas thus that our country was saved;
　　So told us the safety committee!
But psha! I've the heart of a soldier,
　　All gentleness, mercy, and pity.
I loathed to assist at such deeds,
　　And my drum beat its loudest of tunes
As we offered to justice offended
　　The blood of the bloody tribunes.

"Away with such foul recollections!
　　No more of the axe and the block;
I saw the last fight of the sections,
　　As they fell 'neath our guns at Saint Rock.
Young BONAPARTE led us that day;
　　When he sought the Italian frontier,
I follow'd my gallant young captain,
　　I follow'd him many a long year.

"We came to an army in rags,
　　Our general was but a boy
When we first saw the Austrian flags
　　Flaunt proud in the fields of Savoy.
In the glorious year ninety-six,
　　We march'd to the banks of the Po;
I carried my drum and my sticks,
　　And we laid the proud Austrian low.

"In triumph we enter'd Milan,
    We seized on the Mantuan keys ;
The troops of the Emperor ran,
    And the Pope he fell down on his knees."—
Pierre's comrades here call'd a fresh bottle,
    And clubbing together their wealth,
They drank to the Army of Italy,
    And General Bonaparte's health.

The drummer now bared his old breast,
    And show'd us a plenty of scars,
Rude presents that Fortune had made him
    In fifty victorious wars.
"This came when I follow'd bold Kleber—
    'Twas shot by a Mameluke gun ;
And this from an Austrian sabre,
    When the field of Marengo was won.

" My forehead has many deep furrows,
    But this is the deepest of all :
A Brunswicker made it at Jena,
    Beside the fair river of Saal.
This cross, 'twas the Emperor gave it ;
    (God bless him !) it covers a blow ;
I had it at Austerlitz fight,
    As I beat on my drum in the snow.

" 'Twas thus that we conquer'd and fought ;
    But wherefore continue the story ?
There's never a baby in France
    But has heard of our chief and our glory,—
But has heard of our chief and our fame,
    His sorrows and triumphs can tell,
How bravely Napoleon conquer'd,
    How bravely and sadly he fell.

" It makes my old heart to beat higher,
    To think of the deeds that I saw ;
I follow'd bold Ney through the fire,
    And charged at the side of Murat."

And so did old Peter continue
  His story of twenty brave years ;
His audience follow'd with comments—
  Rude comments of curses and tears.

He told how the Prussians in vain
  Had died in defence of their land ;
His audience laugh'd at the story,
  And vow'd that their captain was grand !
He had fought the red English, he said,
  In many a battle of Spain :
They cursed the red English, and prayed
  To meet them and fight them again.

He told them how Russia was lost,
  Had winter not driven them back ;
And his company cursed the quick frost,
  And doubly they cursed the Cossack.
He told how the stranger arrived ;
  They wept at the tale of disgrace ;
And they long'd but for one battle more,
  The stain of their shame to efface.

" Our country their hordes overrun,
  We fled to the fields of Champagne,
And fought them, though twenty to one,
  And beat them again and again !
Our warrior was conquer'd at last ;
  They bade him his crown to resign ;
To fate and his country he yielded
  The rights of himself and his line.

" He came, and among us he stood,
  Around him we press'd in a throng :
We could not regard him for weeping,
  Who had led us and loved us so long.
' I have led you for twenty long years,'
  Napoleon said ere he went ;
' Wherever was honour I found you,
  And with you, my sons, am content !

" ' Though Europe against me was arm'd,
    Your chiefs and my people are true ;
 I still might have struggled with fortune,
    And baffled all Europe with you.

" ' But France would have suffer'd the while,
    'Tis best that I suffer alone ·
 I go to my place of exile,
    To write of the deeds we have done.

" ' Be true to the king that they give you.
    We may not embrace ere we part ;
 But, General, reach me your hand,
    And press me, I pray, to your heart.'

 " He call'd for our battle standard ;
    One kiss to the eagle he gave.
 ' Dear eagle !' he said, ' may this kiss
    Long sound in the hearts of the brave !'
 'Twas thus that Napoleon left us ;
    Our people were weeping and mute,
 As he passed through the lines of his guard,
    And our drums beat the notes of salute.

           *   *   *   *

 " I look'd when the drumming was o'er,
    I look'd, but our hero was gone ;
 We were destined to see him once more,
    When we fought on the Mount of St. John.
 The Emperor rode through our files ;
    'Twas June, and a fair Sunday morn.
 The lines of our warriors for miles
    Stretch'd wide through the Waterloo corn.

 " In thousands we stood on the plain,
    The red-coats were crowning the height ;
 ' Go scatter yon English,' he said ;
    ' We'll sup, lads, at Brussels to-night.'

We answer'd his voice with a shout ;
  Our eagles were bright in the sun ;
Our drums and our cannon spoke out,
  And the thundering battle begun.

" One charge to another succeeds,
  Like waves that a hurricane bears ;
All day do our galloping steeds
  Dash fierce on the enemy's squares.
At noon we began the fell onset :
  We charged up the Englishman's hill ;
And madly we charged it at sunset—
  His banners were floating there still.

" —Go to ! I will tell you no more ;
  You know how the battle was lost.
Ho ! fetch me a beaker of wine,
  And, comrades, I'll give you a toast.
I'll give you a curse on all traitors,
  Who plotted our Emperor's ruin ;
And a curse on those red-coated English,
  Whose bayonets helped our undoing.

" A curse on those British assassins,
  Who order'd the slaughter of Ney ;
A curse on Sir Hudson, who tortured
  The life of our hero away.
A curse on all Russians—I hate them—
  On all Prussian and Austrian fry ;
And oh ! but I pray we may meet them,
  And fight them again ere I die."

'Twas thus old Peter did conclude
  His chronicle with curses fit.
He spoke the tale in accents rude,
  In ruder verse I copied it.

Perhaps the tale a moral bears,
  (All tales in time to this must come,)
The story of two hundred years
  Writ on the parchment of a drum.

What Peter told with drum and stick,
   Is endless theme for poet's pen :
Is found in endless quartos thick,
   Enormous books by learned men.

And ever since historian writ,
   And ever since a bard could sing,
Doth each exalt with all his wit
   The noble art of murdering.

We love to read the glorious page,
   How bold Achilles kill'd his foe ;
And Turnus, fell'd by Trojans' rage,
   Went howling to the shades below.

How Godfrey led his red-cross knights,
   How mad Orlando slash'd and slew ;
There's not a single bard that writes
   But doth the glorious theme renew.

And while, in fashion picturesque,
   The poet rhymes of blood and blows,
The grave historian at his desk
   Describes the same in classic prose.

Go read the works of Reverend Coxe,
   You'll duly see recorded there
The history of the self-same knocks
   Here roughly sung by Drummer Pierre.

Of battles fierce and warriors big,
   He writes in phrases dull and slow,
And waves his cauliflower wig,
   And shouts " Saint George for Marlborow ! "

Take Doctor Southey from the shelf,
   An LL.D.,—a peaceful man ;
Good Lord, how doth he plume himself
   Because we beat the Corsican !

From first to last his page is filled
   With stirring tales how blows were struck.
He shows how we the Frenchmen kill'd,
   And praises God for our good luck.

Some hints, 'tis true, of politics
   The doctor gives and statesman's art :
Pierre only bangs his drum and sticks,
   And understands the bloody part.

He cares not what the cause may be,
   He is not nice for wrong and right ;
But show him where's the enemy,
   He only asks to drum and fight.

They bid him fight,—perhaps he wins ;
   And when he tells the story o'er,
The honest savage brags and grins,
   And only longs to fight once more.

But luck may change, and valour fail,
   Our drummer, Peter, meet reverse,
And with a moral points his tale—
   The end of all such tales—a curse.

Last year, my love, it was my hap
   Behind a grenadier to be,
And, but he wore a hairy cap,
   No taller man, methinks, than me.

Prince Albert and the Queen, God wot,
   (Be blessings on the glorious pair !)
Before us passed. I saw them not—
   I only saw a cap of hair.

Your orthodox historian puts
   In foremost rank the soldier thus,
The red-coat bully in his boots,
   That hides the march of men from us.

He puts him there in foremost rank,
  You wonder at his cap of hair :
You hear his sabre's cursed clank,
  His spurs are jingling everywhere.

Go to ! I hate him and his trade :
  Who bade us so to cringe and bend,
And all God's peaceful people made
  To such as him subservient ?

Tell me what find we to admire
  In epaulets and scarlet coats—
In men, because they load and fire,
  And know the art of cutting throats ?

    *   *   *   *

Ah, gentle, tender lady mine !
  The winter wind blows cold and shrill ;
Come, fill me one more glass of wine,
  And give the silly fools their will.

And what care we for war and wrack,
  How kings and heroes rise and fall ?
Look yonder,* in his coffin black
  There lies the greatest of them all !

To pluck him down, and keep him up,
  Died many million human souls.—
'Tis twelve o'clock and time to sup ;
  Bid Mary heap the fire with coals.

He captured many thousand guns ;
  He wrote " The Great " before his name ;
And dying, only left his sons
  The recollection of his shame.

---

* This ballad was written at Paris at the time of the Second Funeral of Napoleon.

Though more than half the world was his,
   He died without a rood his own ;
And borrow'd from his enemies
   Six foot of ground to lie upon.

He fought a thousand glorious wars,
   And more than half the world was his,
And somewhere now, in yonder stars,
   Can tell, mayhap, what greatness is.

1841.

ABD-EL-KADER AT TOULON.

OR, THE CAGED HAWK.

No more, thou lithe and long-winged hawk, of desert life for thee ;
No more across the sultry sands shalt thou go swooping free :
Blunt idle talons, idle beak, with spurning of thy chain,
Shatter against thy cage the wing thou ne'er may'st spread again.

Long, sitting by their watchfires, shall the Kabyles tell the tale
Of thy dash from Ben Halifa on the fat Metidja vale ;
How thou swept'st the desert over, bearing down the wild El Riff,
From eastern Beni Salah to western Ouad Shelif ;

How thy white burnous went streaming, like the storm-rack o'er the
    sea,
When thou rodest in the vanward of the Moorish chivalry ;
How thy razzia was a whirlwind, thy onset a simoom,
How thy sword-sweep was the lightning, dealing death from out the
    gloom !

Nor less quick to slay in battle than in peace to spare and save,
Of brave men wisest councillor, of wise councillors most brave ;
How the eye that flashed destruction could beam gentleness and love,
How lion in thee mated lamb, how eagle mated dove !

Availèd not or steel or shot 'gainst that charmed life secure,
Till cunning France, in last resource, tossed up the golden lure ;
And the carrion buzzards round him stooped, faithless, to the cast,
And the wild hawk of the desert is caught and caged at last.

Weep, maidens of Zerifah, above the laden loom !
Scar, chieftains of Al Elmah, your cheeks in grief and gloom !
Sons of the Beni Snazam, throw down the useless lance,
And stoop your necks and bare your backs to yoke and scourge of
    France !

'Twas not in fight they bore him down ; he never cried *amàn ;*
He never sank his sword before the PRINCE OF FRANGHISTAN ;
But with traitors all around him, his star upon the wane,
He heard the voice of ALLAH, and he would not strive in vain.

They gave him what he asked them ; from king to king he spake,
As one that plighted word and seal not knoweth how to break :
" Let me pass from out my deserts, be't mine own choice where to go ;
I brook no fettered life to live, a captive and a show."

And they promised, and he trusted them, and proud and calm he
    came,
Upon his black mare riding, girt with his sword of fame.

Good steed, good sword, he rendered both unto the Frankish throng;
He knew them false and fickle—but a Prince's word is strong.

How have they kept their promise?   Turned they the vessel's prow
Unto Acre, Alexandria, as they have sworn e'en now?
Not so : from Oran northwards the white sails gleam and glance,
And the wild hawk of the desert is borne away to France !

Where Toulon's white-walled lazaret looks southward o'er the wave,
Sits he that trusted in the word a son of LOUIS gave.
O noble faith of noble heart !   And was the warning vain,
The text writ by the BOURBON in the blurred black book of Spain?

They have need of thee to gaze on, they have need of thee to grace
The triumph of the Prince, to gild the pinchbeck of their race.
Words are but wind, conditions must be construed by GUIZOT ;
Dash out thy heart, thou desert hawk, ere thou art made a show !

THE KING OF BRENTFORD'S TESTAMENT.

THE noble King of Brentford
    Was old and very sick,
He summon'd his physicians
    To wait upon him quick ;
They stepp'd into their coaches
    And brought their best physick.

They cramm'd their gracious master
    With potion and with pill ;
They drench'd him and they bled him :
    They could not cure his ill.
"Go fetch," says he, "my lawyer ;
    I'd better make my will."

The monarch's royal mandate
    The lawyer did obey ;
The thought of six-and-eightpence
    Did make his heart full gay.
"What is't," says he, "your Majesty
    Would wish of me to-day ?"

" The doctors have belabour'd me
    With potion and with pill :
My hours of life are counted,
    O man of tape and quill !
Sit down and mend a pen or two ;
    I want to make my will.

" O'er all the land of Brentford
    I'm lord, and eke of Kew :
I've three-per-cents and five-per-cents ;
    My debts are but a few ;
And to inherit after me
    I have but children two.

" Prince Thomas is my eldest son ;
   A sober prince is he,
And from the day we breech'd him
   Till now—he's twenty-three—
He never caused disquiet
   To his poor mamma or me.

" At school they never flogg'd him ;
   At college, though not fast,
Yet his little-go and great-go
   He creditably pass'd,
And made his year's allowance
   For eighteen months to last.

" He never owed a shilling,
   Went never drunk to bed,
He has not two ideas
   Within his honest head—
In all respects he differs
   From my second son, Prince Ned.

" When Tom has half his income
   Laid by at the year's end,
Poor Ned has ne'er a stiver
   That rightly he may spend,
But sponges on a tradesman,
   Or borrows from a friend.

" While Tom his legal studies
   Most soberly pursues,
Poor Ned must pass his mornings
   A-dawdling with the Muse :
While Tom frequents his banker,
   Young Ned frequents the Jews.

" Ned drives about in buggies,
   Tom sometimes takes a 'bus ;
Ah, cruel fate, why made you
   My children differ thus ?
Why make of Tom a *dullard*,
   And Ned a *genius ?* "

"You'll cut him with a shilling,"
  Exclaimed the man of wits :
" I'll leave my wealth," said Brentford,
  " Sir Lawyer, as befits,
And portion both their fortunes
  Unto their several wits."

"Your Grace knows best," the lawyer said;
  " On your commands I wait."
" Be silent, Sir," says Brentford,
  " A plague upon your prate !
Come take your pen and paper,
  And write as I dictate."

The will as Brentford spoke it
  Was writ and signed and closed ;
He bade the lawyer leave him,
  And turn'd him round and dozed ;
And next week in the churchyard
  The good old King reposed.

Tom, dressed in crape and hatband,
  Of mourners was the chief ;
In bitter self-upbraidings
  Poor Edward showed his grief :
Tom hid his fat white countenance
  In his pocket-handkerchief.

Ned's eyes were full of weeping,
  He falter'd in his walk ;
Tom never shed a tear,
  But onwards he did stalk,
As pompous, black, and solemn
  As any catafalque.

And when the bones of Brentford—
  That gentle king and just—
With bell and book and candle
  Were duly laid in dust,
"Now, gentlemen," says Thomas,
  " Let business be discussed.

"When late our sire beloved
    Was taken deadly ill,
Sir Lawyer, you attended him
    (I mean to tax your bill) ;
And, as you signed and wrote it,
    I prithee read the will."

The lawyer wiped his spectacles,
    And drew the parchment out ;
And all the Brentford family
    Sat eager round about :
Poor Ned was somewhat anxious,
    But Tom had ne'er a doubt.

" My son, as I make ready
    To seek my last long home,
Some cares I had for Neddy,
    But none for thee, my Tom :
Sobriety and order
    You ne'er departed from.

" Ned hath a brilliant genius,
    And thou a plodding brain ;
On thee I think with pleasure,
    On him with doubt and pain."
(" You see, good Ned," says Thomas,
    " What he thought about us twain.")

" Though small was your allowance,
    You saved a little store ;
And those who. save a little
    Shall get a plenty more."
As the lawyer read this compliment,
    Tom's eyes were running o'er.

" The tortoise and the hare, Tom,
    Set out at each his pace ;
The hare it was the fleeter,
    The tortoise won the race ;
And since the world's beginning
    This ever was the case.

" Ned's genius, blithe and singing,
　　Steps gaily o'er the ground ;
As steadily you trudge it,
　　He clears it with a bound ;
But dulness has stout legs, Tom,
　　And wind that's wondrous sound.

" O'er fruits and flowers alike, Tom,
　　You pass with plodding feet ;
You heed not one nor t'other,
　　But onwards go your beat ;
While genius stops to loiter
　　With all that he may meet ;

" And ever as he wanders,
　　Will have a pretext fine
For sleeping in the morning,
　　Or loitering to dine,
Or dozing in the shade,
　　Or basking in the shine.

" Your little steady eyes, Tom,
　　Though not so bright as those
That restless round about him
　　His flashing genius throws,
Are excellently suited
　　To look before your nose.

" Thank heaven, then, for the blinkers
　　It placed before your eyes ;
The stupidest are strongest,
　　The witty are not wise ;
Oh, bless your good stupidity !
　　It is your dearest prize.

" And though my lands are wide,
　　And plenty is my gold,
Still better gifts from Nature,
　　My Thomas, do you hold—
A brain that's thick and heavy,
　　A heart that's dull and cold.

" Too dull to feel depression,
   Too hard to heed distress,
Too cold to yield to passion
   Or silly tenderness.
March on—your road is open
   To wealth, Tom, and success.

" Ned sinneth in extravagance,
   And you in greedy lust."
(" I' faith," says Ned, " our father
   Is less polite than just.")
" In you, son Tom, I've confidence,
   But Ned I cannot trust.

" Wherefore my lease and copyholds,
   My lands and tenements,
My parks, my farms, and orchards,
   My houses and my rents,
My Dutch stock and my Spanish stock,
   My five and three per cents,

" I leave to you, my Thomas "—
   (" What, all ?" poor Edward said.
" Well, well, I should have spent them,
   And Tom's a prudent head ")—
" I leave to you, my Thomas,—
   To you IN TRUST for Ned."

The wrath and consternation
   What poet e'er could trace
That at this fatal passage
   Came o'er Prince Tom his face ;
The wonder of the company,
   And honest Ned's amaze?

" 'Tis surely some mistake,"
   Good-naturedly cries Ned ;
The lawyer answered gravely,
   " 'Tis even as I said ;
'Twas thus his gracious Majesty
   Ordain'd on his death-bed.

"See, here the will is witness'd.
    And here's his autograph."
"In truth, our father's writing,"
    Says Edward, with a laugh;
"But thou shalt not be a loser, Tom;
    We'll share it half and half."

"Alas! my kind young gentleman,
    This sharing cannot be;
'Tis written in the testament
    That Brentford spoke to me,
'I do forbid Prince Ned to give
    Prince Tom a halfpenny.

"'He hath a store of money,
    But ne'er was known to lend it;
He never helped his brother;
    The poor he ne'er befriended;
He hath no need of property
    Who knows not how to spend it.

"'Poor Edward knows but how to spend,
    And thrifty Tom to hoard;
Let Thomas be the steward then,
    And Edward be the lord;
And as the honest labourer
    Is worthy his reward,

"'I pray Prince Ned, my second son,
    And my successor dear,
To pay to his intendant
    Five hundred pounds a year;
And to think of his old father,
    And live and make good cheer.'"

Such was old Brentford's honest testament,
    He did devise his moneys for the best,
And lies in Brentford church in peaceful rest.
Prince Edward lived, and money made and spent;

But his good sire was wrong, it is confess'd,
To say his son, young Thomas, never lent.
He did.   Young Thomas lent at interest,
And nobly took his twenty-five per cent.

Long time the famous reign of Ned endured
O'er Chiswick, Fulham, Brentford, Putney, Kew,
But of extravagance he ne'er was cured.
And when both died, as mortal men will do,
'Twas commonly reported that the steward
Was very much the richer of the two.

THE WHITE SQUALL.

ON deck, beneath the awning,
I dozing lay and yawning;
It was the grey of dawning,
    Ere yet the sun arose;
And above the funnel's roaring,
And the fitful wind's deploring,
I heard the cabin snoring
    With universal nose.
I could hear the passengers snorting,
I envied their disporting—
Vainly I was courting
    The pleasure of a doze!

So I lay, and wondered why light
Came not, and watched the twilight,
And the glimmer of the skylight,
    That shot across the deck

And the binnacle pale and steady,
And the dull glimpse of the dead-eye,
And the sparks in fiery eddy
    That whirled from the chimney neck.
In our jovial floating prison
There was sleep from fore to mizen,
And never a star had risen
    The hazy sky to speck.

Strange company we harboured ;
We'd a hundred Jews to larboard,
Unwashed, uncombed, unbarbered—
    Jews black, and brown, and gray ;
With terror it would seize ye,
And make your souls uneasy,
To see those Rabbis greasy,
    Who did nought but scratch and pray :
Their dirty children puking—
Their dirty saucepans cooking—
Their dirty fingers hooking
    Their swarming fleas away.

To starboard, Turks and Greeks were—
Whiskered and brown their cheeks were—
Enormous wide their breeks were,
    Their pipes did puff alway ;
Each on his mat allotted
In silence smoked and squatted,
Whilst round their children trotted
    In pretty, pleasant play.
He can't but smile who traces
The smiles on those brown faces,
And the pretty prattling graces
    Of those small heathens gay.

And so the hours kept tolling,
And through the ocean rolling
Went the brave " Iberia " bowling
    Before the break of day——

When A SQUALL, upon a sudden,
Came o'er the waters scudding ;

And the clouds began to gather,
And the sea was lashed to lather,
And the lowering thunder grumbled,
And the lightning jumped and tumbled,
And the ship, and all the ocean,
Woke up in wild commotion.
Then the wind set up a howling,
And the poodle dog a yowling,
And the cocks began a crowing,
And the old cow raised a lowing,
As she heard the tempest blowing ;
And fowls and geese did cackle,
And the cordage and the tackle
Began to shriek and crackle ;
And the spray dashed o'er the funnels,
And down the deck in runnels ;
And the rushing water soaks all,
From the seamen in the fo'ksal
To the stokers whose black faces
Peer out of their bed-places ;
And the captain he was bawling,
And the sailors pulling, hauling,
And the quarter-deck tarpauling
Was shivered in the squalling ;
And the passengers awaken,
Most pitifully shaken ;
And the steward jumps up, and hastens
For the necessary basins.

Then the Greeks they groaned and quivered,
And they knelt, and moaned, and shivered,
As the plunging waters met them,
And splashed and overset them ;
And they call in their emergence
Upon countless saints and virgins ;
And their marrowbones are bended,
And they think the world is ended.
And the Turkish women for'ard
Were frightened and behorror'd ;
And shrieking and bewildering,
The mothers clutched their children ;

The men sang " Allah ! Illah !
Mashallah Bismillah !"
As the warring waters doused them
And splashed them and soused them,
And they called upon the Prophet,
And thought but little of it.

Then all the fleas in Jewry
Jumped up and bit like fury ;
And the progeny of Jacob
Did on the main-deck wake up
(I wot those greasy Rabbins
Would never pay for cabins) ;
And each man moaned and jabbered in
His filthy Jewish gaberdine,
In woe and lamentation,
And howling consternation.
And the splashing water drenches
Their dirty brats and wenches ;
And they crawl from bales and benches
In a hundred thousand stenches.

This was the White Squall famous,
Which latterly o'ercame us,
And which all will well remember
On the 28th September ;
When a Prussian captain of Lancers
(Those tight-laced, whiskered prancers)
Came on the deck astonished,
By that wild squall admonished,
And wondering cried, " Potztausend !
Wie ist der Sturm jetzt brausend?"
And looked at Captain Lewis,
Who calmly stood and blew his
Cigar in all the bustle,
And scorned the tempest's tussle.
And oft we've thought thereafter
How he beat the storm to laughter ;
For well he knew his vessel
With that vain wind could wrestle ;

And when a wreck we thought her,
And doomed ourselves to slaughter,
How gaily he fought her,
And through the hubbub brought her,
And as the tempest caught her,
Cried, " GEORGE ! SOME BRANDY-AND-WATER !"

And when, its force expended,
The harmless storm was ended,
And as the sunrise splendid
   Came blushing o'er the sea,
I thought, as day was breaking,
My little girls were waking,
And smiling, and making
   A prayer at home for me.

1844.

PEG OF LIMAVADDY.

John Collier

RIDING from Coleraine
  (Famed for lovely Kitty),
Came a Cockney bound
  Unto Derry city ;
Weary was his soul,
  Shivering and sad, he
Bumped along the road
  Leads to Limavaddy.

Mountains stretch'd around,
  Gloomy was their tinting,
And the horse's hoofs
  Made a dismal clinting ;

Wind upon the heath
  Howling was and piping,
On the heath and bog,
  Black with many a snipe in.
Mid the bogs of black,
  Silver pools were flashing,
Crows upon their sides
  Pecking were and splashing.
Cockney on the car
  Closer folds his plaidy,
Grumbling at the road
  Leads to Limavaddy.

Through the crashing woods
  Autumn brawl'd and bluster'd,
Tossing round about
  Leaves the hue of mustard ;
Yonder lay Lough Foyle,
  Which a storm was whipping,
Covering with mist
  Lake, and shores, and shipping.
Up and down the hill
  (Nothing could be bolder),
Horse went with a raw
  Bleeding on his shoulder.
" Where are horses changed? "
  Said I to the laddy
Driving on the box :
  " Sir, at Limavaddy."

Limavaddy inn's
  But a humble bait house,
Where you may procure
  Whisky and potatoes ;
Landlord at the door
  Gives a smiling welcome
To the shivering wights
  Who to his hotel come.
Landlady within
  Sits and knits a stocking,
With a wary foot
  Baby's cradle rocking.

To the chimney nook
  Having found admittance,
There I watch a pup
  Playing with two kittens ;
(Playing round the fire,
  Which of blazing turf is,
Roaring to the pot
  Which bubbles with the murphies.)
And the cradled babe
  Fond the mother nursed it,
Singing it a song
  As she twists the worsted !

Up and down the stair
  Two more young ones patter
(Twins were never seen
  Dirtier or fatter).
Both have mottled legs,
  Both have snubby noses,
Both have——Here the host
  Kindly interposes :
" Sure you must be froze
  With the sleet and hail, sir :
So will you have some punch,
  Or will you have some ale, sir? "

Presently a maid
  Enters with the liquor
(Half a pint of ale
  Frothing in a beaker).
Gads ! I didn't know
  What my beating heart meant :
Hebe's self, I thought,
  Entered the apartment.
As she came she smiled,
  And the smile bewitching,
On my word and honour,
  Lighted all the kitchen !
With a curtsey neat
  Greeting the new comer,
Lovely, smiling Peg
  Offers me the rummer ;

But my trembling hand
  Up the beaker tilted,
And the glass of ale
  Every drop I spilt it :
Spilt it every drop
  (Dames, who read my volumes,
Pardon such a word)
  On my what-d'ye-call-'ems !

Witnessing the sight
  Of that dire disaster,
Out began to laugh
  Missis, maid, and master ;
Such a merry peal
  'Specially Miss Peg's was,
(As the glass of ale
  Trickling down my legs was,)
That the joyful sound
  Of that mingling laughter
Echoed in my ears
  Many a long day after.

Such a silver peal !
  In the meadows listening,
You who've heard the bells
  Ringing to a christening ;
You who ever heard
  Caradori pretty,
Smiling like an angel,
  Singing " Giovinetti ; "
Fancy Peggy's laugh,
  Sweet, and clear, and cheerful,
At my pantaloons
  With half a pint of beer full !

When the laugh was done,
  Peg, the pretty hussy,
Moved about the room
  Wonderfully busy ;
Now she looks to see
  If the kettle keep hot ;

Now she rubs the spoons
    Now she cleans the teapot ;
Now she sets the cups
    Trimly and secure :
Now she scours a pot,
    And so it was I drew her.

Thus it was I drew her
    Scouring of a kettle,
(Faith ! her blushing cheeks
    Redden'd on the metal !)
Ah ! but 'tis in vain
    That I try to sketch it ;
The pot perhaps is like,
    But Peggy's face is wretched.
No ! the best of lead
    And of india-rubber
Never could depict
    That sweet kettle-scrubber !

See her as she moves,
    Scarce the ground she touches,
Airy as a fay,
    Graceful as a duchess
Bare her rounded arm,
    Bare her little leg is,
Vestris never show'd
    Ankles like to Peggy's.
Braided is her hair,
    Soft her look and modest,
Slim her little waist
    Comfortably bodiced.

This I do declare,
    Happy is the laddy
Who the heart can share
    Of Peg of Limavaddy.
Married if she were
    Blest would be the daddy
Of the children fair
    Of Peg of Limavaddy.

Beauty is not rare
In the land of Paddy,
Fair beyond compare
Is Peg of Limavaddy.

Citizen or Squire,
Tory, Whig, or Radi-
cal would all desire
Peg of Limavaddy.
Had I Homer's fire,
Or that of Serjeant Taddy,
Meetly I'd admire
Peg of Limavaddy.
And till I expire,
Or till I grow mad, I
Will sing unto my lyre
Peg of Limavaddy !

MAY-DAY ODE.

BUT yesterday a naked sod
  The dandies sneered from Rotten Row,
  And cantered o'er it to and fro :
            And see 'tis done !
As though 'twere by a wizard's rod
  A blazing arch of lucid glass
  Leaps like a fountain from the grass
            To meet the sun !

A quiet green but few days since,
  With cattle browsing in the shade :
  And here are lines of bright arcade
            In order raised !
A palace as for fairy prince,
  A rare pavilion, such as man
  Saw never since mankind began,
            And built and glazed !

A peaceful place it was but now,
  And lo ! within its shining streets
  A multitude of nations meets ;
            A countless throng
I see beneath the crystal bow,
  And Gaul and German, Russ and Turk,
  Each with his native handiwork
            And busy tongue.

I felt a thrill of love and awe
  To mark the different garb of each,
  The changing tongue, the various speech
            Together blent :

A thrill, methinks, like His who saw
  " All people dwelling upon earth
  Praising our God with solemn mirth
          And one consent."

High Sovereign, in your Royal state,
  Captains, and chiefs, and councillors,
  Before the lofty palace doors
          Are open set,—
Hush ! ere you pass the shining gate ;
  Hush ! ere the heaving curtain draws,
  And let the Royal pageant pause
          A moment yet.

People and prince a silence keep !
  Bow coronet and kingly crown,
  Helmet and plume, bow lowly down,
          The while the priest,
Before the splendid portal step,
  (While still the wondrous banquet stays,)
  From Heaven supreme a blessing prays
          Upon the feast.

Then onwards let the triumph march ;
  Then let the loud artillery roll,
  And trumpets ring, and joy-bells toll,
          And pass the gate.
Pass underneath the shining arch,
  'Neath which the leafy elms are green ;
  Ascend unto your throne, O Queen !
          And take your state.

Behold her in her Royal place ;
  A gentle lady ; and the hand
  That sways the sceptre of this land,
          How frail and weak !
Soft is the voice, and fair the face :
  She breathes amen to prayer and hymn ;
  No wonder that her eyes are dim,
          And pale her cheek.

This moment round her empire's shores
   The winds of Austral winter sweep,
   And thousands lie in midnight sleep
           At rest to-day.
Oh! awful is that crown of yours,
   Queen of innumerable realms
   Sitting beneath the budding elms
           Of English May!

A wondrous sceptre 'tis to bear:
   Strange mystery of God which set
   Upon her brow yon coronet,—
           The foremost crown
Of all the world, on one so fair!
   That chose her to it from her birth,
   And bade the sons of all the earth
           To her bow down.

The representatives of man
   Here from the far Antipodes,
   And from the subject Indian seas,
           In Congress meet;
From Afric and from Hindustan,
   From Western continent and isle,
   The envoys of her empire pile
           Gifts at her feet;

Our brethren cross the Atlantic tides,
   Loading the gallant decks which once
   Roared a defiance to our guns,
           With peaceful store;
Symbol of peace, their vessel rides!*
   O'er English waves float Star and Stripe,
   And firm their friendly anchors gripe
           The father shore!

From Rhine and Danube, Rhone and Seine,
   As rivers from their sources gush,
   The swelling floods of nations rush,
           And seaward pour:

* The U.S. frigate " St. Lawrence."

From coast to coast in friendly chain,
  With countless ships we bridge the straits,
  And angry ocean separates
      Europe no more.

From Mississippi and from Nile—
  From Baltic, Ganges, Bosphorus,
  In England's ark assembled thus
      Are friend and guest.
Look down the mighty sunlit aisle,
  And see the sumptuous banquet set,
  The brotherhood of nations met
      Around the feast !

Along the dazzling colonnade,
  Far as the straining eye can gaze,
  Gleam cross and fountain, bell and vase,
      In vistas bright ;
And statues fair of nymph and maid,
  And steeds and pards and Amazons,
  Writhing and grappling in the bronze,
      In endless fight.

To deck the glorious roof and dome,
  To make the Queen a canopy,
  The peaceful hosts of industry
      Their standards bear.
Yon are the works of Brahmin loom ;
  On such a web of Persian thread
  The desert Arab bows his head
      And cries his prayer.

Look yonder where the engines toil :
  These England's arms of conquest are,
  The trophies of her bloodless war :
      Brave weapons these.
Victorious over wave and soil,
  With these she sails, she weaves, she tills,
  Pierces the everlasting hills
      And spans the seas.

The engine roars upon its race,
  The shuttle whirrs along the woof,
  The people hum from floor to roof,
      With Babel tongue.
The fountain in the basin plays,
  The chanting organ echoes clear,
  An awful chorus 'tis to hear,
      A wondrous song!

Swell, organ, swell your trumpet blast,
  March, Queen and Royal pageant, march
  By splendid aisle and springing arch
      Of this fair Hall :
And see! above the fabric vast,
  God's boundless heaven is bending blue,
  God's peaceful sunlight's beaming through,
      And shines o'er all.

May, 1851.

THE BALLAD OF BOUILLABAISSE.

A STREET there is in Paris famous,
  For which no rhyme our language yields,
Rue Neuve des Petits Champs its name is—
  The New Street of the Little Fields.
And here's an inn, not rich and splendid,
  But still in comfortable case ;
The which in youth I oft attended,
  To eat a bowl of Bouillabaisse.

This Bouillabaisse a noble dish is—
  A sort of soup or broth, or brew,
Or hotchpotch of all sorts of fishes,
  That Greenwich never could outdo ;
Green herbs, red peppers, mussels, saffron,
  Soles, onions, garlic, roach, and dace :
All these you eat at TERRE's tavern,
  In that one dish of Bouillabaisse.

Indeed, a rich and savoury stew 'tis ;
  And true philosophers, methinks,
Who love all sorts of natural beauties,
  Should love good victuals and good drinks.
And Cordelier or Benedictine
  Might gladly, sure, his lot embrace,
Nor find a fast-day too afflicting,
  Which served him up a Bouillabaisse.

I wonder if the house still there is ?
  Yes, here the lamp is, as before ;
The smiling red-cheeked *écaillère* is
  Still opening oysters at the door.

Is TERRÉ still alive and able?
    I recollect his droll grimace :
He'd come and smile before your table,
    And hope you liked your Bouillabaisse.

We enter—nothing's changed or older.
    " How's Monsieur TERRÉ, waiter, pray ? "
The waiter stares and shrugs his shoulder—
    " Monsieur is dead this many a day."
" It is the lot of saint and sinner,
    So honest TERRÉ's run his race."
" What will Monsieur require for dinner ? "
    " Say, do you still cook Bouillabaisse ? "

" Oh, oui, Monsieur," 's the waiter's answer;
    " Quel vin Monsieur désire-t-il ? "
" Tell me a good one."—" That I can, Sir :
    The Chambertin with yellow seal."
" So TERRÉ's gone," I say, and sink in
    My old accustom'd corner-place;
" He's done with feasting and with drinking,
    With Burgundy and Bouillabaisse."

My old accustom'd corner here is,
    The table still is in the nook ;
Ah ! vanish'd many a busy year is
    This well-known chair since last I took.
When first I saw ye, *cari luoghi*,
    I'd scarce a beard upon my face,
And now a grizzled, grim old fogy,
    I sit and wait for Bouillabaisse.

Where are you, old companions trusty
    Of early days here met to dine ?
Come, waiter ! quick, a flagon crusty—
    I'll pledge them in the good old wine.
The kind old voices and old faces
    My memory can quick retrace ;
Around the board they take their places,
    And share the wine and Bouillabaisse.

There's JACK has made a wondrous marriage;
   There's laughing TOM is laughing yet;
There's brave AUGUSTUS drives his carriage;
   There's poor old FRED in the *Gazette;*
On JAMES'S head the grass is growing:
   Good Lord! the world has wagged apace
Since here we set the claret flowing,
   And drank, and ate the Bouillabaisse.

Ah me! how quick the days are flitting!
   I mind me of a time that's gone,
When here I'd sit, as now I'm sitting,
   In this same place—but not alone.
A fair young form was nestled near me,
   A dear, dear face looked fondly up,
And sweetly spoke and smiled to cheer me
   —There's no one now to share my cup.

     *   *   *   *

I drink it as the Fates ordain it.
   Come, fill it, and have done with rhymes:
Fill up the lonely glass, and drain it
   In memory of dear old times.
Welcome the wine, whate'er the seal is;
   And sit you down and say your grace
With thankful heart, whate'er the meal is.
   —Here comes the smoking Bouillabaisse!

THE MAHOGANY TREE.

CHRISTMAS is here :
Winds whistle shrill,
Icy and chill,
Little care we :
Little we fear
Weather without,
Sheltered about
The Mahogany Tree.

Once on the boughs
Birds of rare plume
Sang, in its bloom ;
Night-birds are we :
Here we carouse,
Singing like them,
Perched round the stem
Of the jolly old tree.

Here let us sport,
Boys, as we sit ;
Laughter and wit
Flashing so free.
Life is but short—
When we are gone,
Let them sing on
Round the old tree.

Evenings we knew,
Happy as this ;
Faces we miss,
Pleasant to see.

Kind hearts and true,
Gentle and just,
Peace to your dust!
We sing round the tree.

Care, like a dun,
Lurks at the gate:
Let the dog wait;
Happy we'll be!
Drink, every one;
Pile up the coals,
Fill the red bowls,
Round the old tree!

Drain we the cup.—
Friend, art afraid?
Spirits are laid
In the Red Sea.
Mantle it up;
Empty it yet;
Let us forget,
Round the old tree.

Sorrows, begone!
Life and its ills,
Duns and their bills,
Bid we to flee.
Come with the dawn,
Blue-devil sprite,
Leave us to-night,
Round the old tree.

THE YANKEE VOLUNTEERS.

"A surgeon of the United States' army says, that on inquiring of the Captain of his company, he found that *nine-tenths* of the men had enlisted on account of some female difficulty."—*Morning Paper.*

YE Yankee volunteers !
It makes my bosom bleed
When I your story read,
 Though oft 'tis told one.
So—in both hemispheres
The women are untrue,
And cruel in the New,
 As in the Old one !

What—in this company
Of sixty sons of Mars,
Who march 'neath Stripes and Stars,
 With fife and horn,
Nine-tenths of all we see
Along the warlike line
Had but one cause to join
 This Hope Forlorn ?

Deserters from the realm
Where tyrant Venus reigns,
You slipp'd her wicked chains,
 Fled and outran her.
And now, with sword and helm,
Together banded are
Beneath the Stripe and Star-
 Embroider'd banner !

And is it so with all
The warriors ranged in line,
With lace bedizen'd fine
 And swords gold-hilted ?

Yon lusty corporal,
Yon colour-man who gripes
The flag of Stars and Stripes—
     Has each been jilted?

Come, each man of this line,
The privates strong and tall,
" The pioneers and all,"
     The fifer nimble—
Lieutenant and Ensign,
Captain with epaulets,
And Blacky there, who beats
     The clanging cymbal—

O cymbal-beating black,
Tell us, as thou canst feel,
Was it some Lucy Neal
     Who caused thy ruin?
O nimble fifing Jack,
And drummer making din
So deftly on the skin,
     With thy rat-tattooing—

Confess, ye volunteers,
Lieutenant and Ensign,
And Captain of the line,
     As bold as Roman—
Confess, ye grenadiers,
However strong and tall,
The Conqueror of you all
     Is Woman, Woman !

No corselet is so proof
But through it from her bow
The shafts that she can throw
     Will pierce and rankle.
No champion e'er so tough,
But 's in the struggle thrown,
And tripp'd and trodden down
     By her slim ankle.

Thus always it was ruled :
And when a woman smiled,
The strong man was a child,
    The sage a noodle.
Alcides was befool'd,
And silly Samson shorn,
Long, long ere you were born,
    Poor Yankee Doodle !

THE PEN AND THE ALBUM.

"I AM Miss Catherine's book," the Album speaks ;
"I've lain among your tomes these many weeks ;
I'm tired of their old coats and yellow cheeks.

"Quick, Pen ! and write a line with a good grace :
Come ! draw me off a funny little face ;
And, prithee, send me back to Chesham Place."

PEN.

"I am my master's faithful old Gold Pen ;
I've served him three long years, and drawn since then
Thousands of funny women and droll men.

"O Album ! could I tell you all his ways
And thoughts, since I am his, these thousand days,
Lord, how your pretty pages I'd amaze !"

ALBUM.

"His ways ? his thoughts ?   Just whisper me a few ;
Tell me a curious anecdote or two,
And write 'em quickly off, good Mordan, do !"

PEN.

"Since he my faithful service did engage
To follow him through his queer pilgrimage,
I've drawn and written many a line and page.

"Caricatures I scribbled have, and rhymes,
And dinner-cards, and picture pantomimes,
And merry little children's books at times.

"I've writ the foolish fancy of his brain ;
 The aimless jest that, striking, hath caused pain ;
 The idle word that he'd wish back again.

  *   *   *   *

"I've help'd him to pen many a line for bread ;
 To joke, with sorrow aching in his head ;
 And make your laughter when his own heart bled.

"I've spoke with men of all degree and sort—
 Peers of the land, and ladies of the Court ;
 Oh, but I've chronicled a deal of sport !

"Feasts that were ate a thousand days ago,
 Biddings to wine that long hath ceased to flow,
 Gay meetings with good fellows long laid low ;

"Summons to bridal, banquet, burial, ball,
 Tradesmen's polite reminders of his small
 Account due Christmas last—I've answer'd all.

"Poor Diddler's tenth petition for a half-
 Guinea ; Miss Bunyan's for an autograph ;
 So I refuse, accept, lament, or laugh,

"Condole, congratulate, invite, praise, scoff,
 Day after day still dipping in my trough,
 And scribbling pages after pages off.

"Day after day the labour's to be done,
 And sure as come the postman and the sun,
 The indefatigable ink must run.

  *   *   *   *

"Go back, my pretty little gilded tome,
 To a fair mistress and a pleasant home,
 Where soft hearts greet us whensoe'er we come !

"Dear, friendly eyes, with constant kindness lit,
 However rude my verse, or poor my wit,
 Or sad or gay my mood, you welcome it.

"Kind lady ! till my last of lines is penn'd,
   My master's love, grief, laughter, at an end,
   Whene'er I write your name, may I write friend !

" Not all are so that were so in past years ;
   Voices, familiar once, no more he hears ;
   Names, often writ, are blotted out in tears.

"So be it :—joys will end and tears will dry——
   Album ! my master bids me wish good-by,
   He'll send you to your mistress presently.

"And thus with thankful heart he closes you :
   Blessing the happy hour when a friend he knew
   So gentle, and so generous, and so true.

"Nor pass the words as idle phrases by ;
   Stranger ! I never writ a flattery,
   Nor sign'd the page that register'd a lie."

MRS. KATHERINE'S LANTERN.

WRITTEN IN A LADY'S ALBUM.

"COMING from a gloomy court,
Place of Israelite resort,
This old lamp I've brought with me.
Madam, on its panes you'll see
The initials K and E."

"An old lantern brought to me?
Ugly, dingy, battered, black!"
(Here a lady I suppose
Turning up a pretty nose)—
"Pray, sir, take the old thing back.
I've no taste for *bric-à-brac.*"

"Please to mark the letters twain"—
(I'm supposed to speak again)—
"Graven on the lantern pane.
Can you tell me who was she,
Mistress of the flowery wreath,
And the anagram beneath—
The mysterious K E?

"Full a hundred years are gone
Since the little beacon shone
From a Venice balcony:
There, on summer nights, it hung,
And her lovers came and sung
To their beautiful K E.

"Hush! in the canal below
Don't you hear the plash of oars
Underneath the lantern's glow,
And a thrilling voice begins
To the sound of mandolins?—
Begins singing of amore
And delire and dolore—
O the ravishing tenore!

"Lady, do you know the tune?
Ah, we all of us have hummed it!
I've an old guitar has thrummed it,
Under many a changing moon.
Shall I try it?   *Do* RE MI * *
What is this?   *Ma foi,* the fact is,
That my hand is out of practice,
And my poor old fiddle cracked is,

And a man—I let the truth out,—
Who's had almost every tooth out,
Cannot sing as once he sung,
When he was young as you are young,
When he was young and lutes were strung,
And love-lamps in the casement hung."

LUCY'S BIRTHDAY.

SEVENTEEN rose-buds in a ring,
Thick with sister flowers beset,
In a fragrant coronet,
Lucy's servants this day bring.
Be it the birthday wreath she wears
Fresh and fair, and symbolling
The young number of her years,
The sweet blushes of her spring.

Types of youth and love and hope !
Friendly hearts your mistress greet,
Be you ever fair and sweet,
And grow lovelier as you ope !
Gentle nurseling, fenced about
With fond care, and guarded so,
Scarce you've heard of storms without,
Frosts that bite, or winds that blow !

Kindly has your life begun,
And we pray that Heaven may send
To our floweret a warm sun,
A calm summer, a sweet end.
And where'er shall be her home,
May she decorate the place ;
Still expanding into bloom,
And developing in grace.

THE CANE-BOTTOM'D CHAIR.

In tattered old slippers that toast at the bars,
And a ragged old jacket perfumed with cigars,
Away from the world and its toils and its cares,
I've a snug little kingdom up four pair of stairs.

To mount to this realm is a toil, to be sure,
But the fire there is bright and the air rather pure;
And the view I behold on a sunshiny day
Is grand through the chimney-pots over the way.

This snug little chamber is cramm'd in all nooks
With worthless old knicknacks and silly old books,

And foolish old odds and foolish old ends,
Crack'd bargains from brokers, cheap keepsakes from friends.

Old armour, prints, pictures, pipes, china, (all crack'd,)
Old rickety tables, and chairs broken-backed ;
A twopenny treasury, wondrous to see ;
What matter ? 'tis pleasant to you, friend, and me.

No better divan need the Sultan require,
Than the creaking old sofa that basks by the fire ;
And 'tis wonderful, surely, what music you get
From the rickety, ramshackle, wheezy spinet.

That praying-rug came from a Turcoman's camp ;
By Tiber once twinkled that brazen old lamp ;
A Mameluke fierce yonder dagger has drawn :
'Tis a murderous knife to toast muffins upon.

Long, long through the hours, and the night, and the chimes,
Here we talk of old books, and old friends, and old times ;
As we sit in a fog made of rich Latakie
This chamber is pleasant to you, friend, and me.

But of all the cheap treasures that garnish my nest,
There's one that I love and I cherish the best :
For the finest of couches that's padded with hair
I never would change thee, my cane-bottom'd chair.

'Tis a bandy-legg'd, high-shoulder'd, worm-eaten seat,
With a creaking old back, and twisted old feet ;
But since the fair morning when Fanny sat there,
I bless thee and love thee, old cane-bottom'd chair.

If chairs have but feeling, in holding such charms,
A thrill must have pass'd through your wither'd old arms !
I look'd, and I long'd, and I wish'd in despair ;
I wish'd myself turn'd to a cane-bottom'd chair.

It was but a moment she sat in this place,
She'd a scarf on her neck, and a smile on her face !
A smile on her face, and a rose in her hair,
And she sat there, and bloom'd in my cane-bottom'd chair.

And so I have valued my chair ever since,
Like the shrine of a saint, or the throne of a prince ;
Saint Fanny, my patroness sweet I declare,
The queen of my heart and my cane-bottom'd chair.

When the candles burn low, and the company's gone,
In the silence of night as I sit here alone—
I sit here alone, but we yet are a pair—
My Fanny I see in my cane-bottom'd chair.

She comes from the past and revisits my room ;
She looks as she then did, all beauty and bloom ;
So smiling and tender, so fresh and so fair,
And yonder she sits in my cane-bottom'd chair.

PISCATOR AND PISCATRIX.

LINES WRITTEN TO AN ALBUM PRINT.

As on this pictured page I look,
This pretty tale of line and hook
As though it were a novel-book
    Amuses and engages :
I know them both, the boy and girl ;
She is the daughter of the Earl,
The lad (that has his hair in curl)
    My lord the County's page is.

A pleasant place for such a pair!
The fields lie basking in the glare;
No breath of wind the heavy air
　　　　Of lazy summer quickens.
Hard by you see the castle tall;
The village nestles round the wall,
As round about the hen its small
　　　　Young progeny of chickens.

It is too hot to pace the keep;
To climb the turret is too steep;
My lord the Earl is dozing deep,
　　　　His noonday dinner over:
The postern-warder is asleep
(Perhaps they've bribed him not to peep):
And so from out the gate they creep,
　　　　And cross the fields of clover.

Their lines into the brook they launch;
He lays his cloak upon a branch,
To guarantee his Lady Blanche
　　　　's delicate complexion:
He takes his rapier from his haunch,
That beardless doughty champion staunch;
He'd drill it through the rival's paunch
　　　　That question'd his affection!

O heedless pair of sportsmen slack!
You never mark, though trout or jack,
Or little foolish stickleback,
　　　　Your baited snares may capture.
What care has *she* for line and hook?
She turns her back upon the brook,
Upon her lover's eyes to look
　　　　In sentimental rapture.

O loving pair! as thus I gaze
Upon the girl who smiles always,
The little hand that ever plays
　　　　Upon the lover's shoulder;

In looking at your pretty shapes,
A sort of envious wish escapes
(Such as the Fox had for the Grapes)
    The Poet your beholder.

To be brave, handsome, twenty-two ;
With nothing else on earth to do,
But all day long to bill and coo :
    It were a pleasant calling.
And had I such a partner sweet ;
A tender heart for mine to beat,
A gentle hand my clasp to meet ;—
I'd let the world flow at my feet,
    And never heed its brawling.

THE ROSE UPON MY BALCONY.

THE rose upon my balcony the morning air perfuming,
Was leafless all the winter time and pining for the spring;
You ask me why her breath is sweet, and why her cheek is blooming:
It is because the sun is out and birds begin to sing.

The nightingale, whose melody is through the greenwood ringing,
Was silent when the boughs were bare and winds were blowing keen:
And if, Mamma, you ask of me the reason of his singing,
It is because the sun is out and all the leaves are green.

Thus each performs his part, Mamma : the birds have found their
    voices,
The blowing rose a flush, Mamma, her bonny cheek to dye ;
And there's sunshine in my heart, Mamma, which wakens and rejoices,
And so I sing and blush, Mamma, and that's the reason why.

RONSARD TO HIS MISTRESS.

" Quand vous serez bien vieille, au soir à la chandelle,
    Assise auprès du feu devisant et filant,
    Direz, chantant mes vers en vous esmerveillant :
Ronsard me célébroit du temps que j'étois belle."

SOME winter night, shut snugly in
    Beside the fagot in the hall,
I think I see you sit and spin,
    Surrounded by your maidens all.
Old tales are told, old songs are sung,
    Old days come back to memory ;
You say, " When I was fair and young,
    A poet sang of me ! "

There's not a maiden in your hall,
    Though tired and sleepy ever so,
But wakes, as you my name recall,
    And longs the history to know.
And, as the piteous tale is said,
    Of lady cold and lover true,
Each, musing, carries it to bed,
    And sighs and envies you !

" Our lady's old and feeble now,"
    They'll say ; " she once was fresh and fair,
And yet she spurn'd her lover's vow,
    And heartless left him to despair:
The lover lies in silent earth,
    No kindly mate the lady cheers :
She sits beside a lonely hearth,
    With threescore and ten years ! "

Ah ! dreary thoughts and dreams are those,
   But wherefore yield me to despair,
While yet the poet's bosom glows,
   While yet the dame is peerless fair ?
Sweet lady mine ! while yet 'tis time
   Requite my passion and my truth,
And gather in their blushing prime
   The roses of your youth !

AT THE CHURCH GATE.

ALTHOUGH I enter not,
Yet round about the spot
    Ofttimes I hover:
And near the sacred gate,
With longing eyes I wait,
    Expectant of her.

The Minster bell tolls out
Above the city's rout,
 And noise and humming:
They've hush'd the Minster bell:
The organ 'gins to swell:
 She's coming, she's coming!

My lady comes at last,
Timid, and stepping fast,
 And hastening hither,
With modest eyes downcast:
She comes—she's here—she's past—
 May heaven go with her!

Kneel, undisturb'd, fair Saint!
Pour out your praise or plaint
 Meekly and duly;
I will not enter there,
To sully your pure prayer
 With thoughts unruly.

But suffer me to pace
Round the forbidden place,
 Lingering a minute
Like outcast spirits who wait
And see through heaven's gate
 Angels within it.

THE AGE OF WISDOM.

HO, pretty page, with the dimpled chin,
   That never has known the barber's shear,
All your wish is woman to win,
This is the way that boys begin,—
   Wait till you come to Forty Year.

Curly gold locks cover foolish brains,
   Billing and cooing is all your cheer ;
Sighing and singing of midnight strains,
Under Bonnybell's window panes,—
   Wait till you come to Forty Year.

Forty times over let Michaelmas pass,
  Grizzling hair the brain doth clear—
Then you know a boy is an ass,
Then you know the worth of a lass,
  Once you have come to Forty Year.

Pledge me round, I bid ye declare,
  All good fellows whose beards are grey,
Did not the fairest of the fair
Common grow and wearisome ere
  Ever a month was pass'd away?

The reddest lips that ever have kissed,
  The brightest eyes that ever have shone,
May pray and whisper, and we not list,
Or look away, and never be missed,
  Ere yet ever a month is gone.

Gillian's dead, God rest her bier,
  How I loved her twenty years syne!
Marian's married, but I sit here
Alone and merry at Forty Year,
  Dipping my nose in the Gascon wine.

SORROWS OF WERTHER.

WERTHER had a love for Charlotte
  Such as words could never utter;
Would you know how first he met her?
  She was cutting bread and butter.

Charlotte was a married lady,
  And a moral man was Werther,
And, for all the wealth of Indies,
  Would do nothing for to hurt her.

So he sighed and pined and ogled,
  And his passion boiled and bubbled,
Till he blew his silly brains out,
  And no more was by it troubled.

Charlotte, having seen his body
  Borne before her on a shutter,
Like a well-conducted person,
  Went on cutting bread and butter.

A DOE IN THE CITY.

LITTLE KITTY LORIMER,
   Fair, and young, and witty,
What has brought your ladyship
   Rambling to the City?

All the Stags in Capel Court
   Saw her lightly trip it;
All the lads of Stock Exchange
   Twigg'd her muff and tippet.

With a sweet perplexity,
  And a mystery pretty,
Threading through Threadneedle Street,
  Trots the little KITTY.

What was my astonishment—
  What was my compunction,
When she reached the Offices
  Of the Didland Junction!

Up the Didland stairs she went,
  To the Didland door, Sir;
Porters, lost in wonderment,
  Let her pass before, Sir.

" Madam," says the old chief Clerk,
  " Sure we can't admit ye."
" Where's the Didland Junction deed?"
  Dauntlessly says KITTY.

" If you doubt my honesty,
  Look at my receipt, Sir."
Up then jumps the old chief Clerk,
  Smiling as he meets her.

KITTY at the table sits
  (Whither the old Clerk leads her),
" *I deliver this*," she says,
  " *As my act and deed, Sir.*"

When I heard these funny words
  Come from lips so pretty,
This, I thought, should surely be
  Subject for a ditty.

What! are ladies stagging it?
  Sure, the more's the pity;
But I've lost my heart to her,—
  Naughty little KITTY.

THE LAST OF MAY.

(IN REPLY TO AN INVITATION DATED ON THE 1ST.)

By fate's benevolent award,
    Should I survive the day,
I'll drink a bumper with my lord
    Upon the last of May.

That I may reach that happy time
    The kindly gods I pray,
For are not ducks and peas in prime
    Upon the last of May ?

At thirty boards, 'twixt now and then,
    My knife and fork shall play ;
But better wine and better men
    I shall not meet in May.

And though, good friend, with whom I dine,
    Your honest head is grey,
And, like this grizzled head of mine,
    Has seen its last of May ;

Yet, with a heart that's ever kind,
    A gentle spirit gay,
You've spring perennial in your mind,
    And round you make a May !

"*AH, BLEAK AND BARREN WAS THE MOOR.*"

Ah ! bleak and barren was the moor,
   Ah ! loud and piercing was the storm,
The cottage roof was sheltered sure,
   The cottage hearth was bright and warm
An orphan-boy the lattice pass'd,
   And, as he marked its cheerful glow,
Felt doubly keen the midnight blast,
   And doubly cold the fallen snow.

They marked him as he onward press'd,
   With fainting heart and weary limb ;
Kind voices bade him turn and rest,
   And gentle faces welcomed him.
The dawn is up—the guest is gone,
   The cottage hearth is blazing still :
Heaven pity all poor wanderers lone !
   Hark to the wind upon the hill !

SONG OF THE VIOLET.

A HUMBLE flower long time I pined
   Upon the solitary plain,
And trembled at the angry wind,
   And shrunk before the bitter rain.

And oh ! 'twas in a blessed hour
   A passing wanderer chanced to see,
And, pitying the lonely flower,
   To stoop and gather me.

I fear no more the tempest rude,
   On dreary heath no more I pine,
But left my cheerless solitude,
   To deck the breast of Caroline.
Alas ! our days are brief at best,
   Nor long, I fear, will mine endure,
Though sheltered here upon a breast
   So gentle and so pure.

It draws the fragrance from my leaves,
   It robs me of my sweetest breath,
And every time it falls and heaves,
   It warns me of my coming death.
But one I know would glad forego
   All joys of life to be as I ;
An hour to rest on that sweet breast,
   And then, contented, die.

FAIRY DAYS.

BESIDE the old hall-fire—upon my nurse's knee,
Of happy fairy days—what tales were told to me!
I thought the world was once—all peopled with princesses,
And my heart would beat to hear—their loves and their distresses;
And many a quiet night,—in slumber sweet and deep,
The pretty fairy people—would visit me in sleep.

I saw them in my dreams—come flying east and west,
With wondrous fairy gifts—the new-born babe they bless'd;
One has brought a jewel—and one a crown of gold,
And one has brought a curse—but she is wrinkled and old.
The gentle queen turns pale—to hear those words of sin,
But the king he only laughs—and bids the dance begin.

The babe has grown to be—the fairest of the land,
And rides the forest green—a hawk upon her hand,

An ambling palfrey white—a golden robe and crown :
I've seen her in my dreams—riding up and down :
And heard the ogre laugh—as she fell into his snare,
At the little tender creature—who wept and tore her hair !

But ever when it seemed—her need was at the sorest,
A prince in shining mail—comes prancing through the forest,
A waving ostrich-plume—a buckler burnished bright ;
I've seen him in my dreams—good sooth ! a gallant knight.
His lips are coral red—beneath a dark moustache ;
See how he waves his hand—and how his blue eyes flash !

" Come forth, thou Paynim knight ! "—he shouts in accents clear.
The giant and the maid—both tremble his voice to hear.
Saint Mary guard him well !—he draws his falchion keen,
The giant and the knight—are fighting on the green.
I see them in my dreams—his blade gives stroke on stroke,
The giant pants and reels—and tumbles like an oak !

With what a blushing grace—he falls upon his knee
And takes the lady's hand—and whispers, " You are free ! "
Ah ! happy childish tales—of knight and faërie !
I waken from my dreams—but there's ne'er a knight for me ;
I waken from my dreams—and wish that I could be
A child by the old hall-fire—upon my nurse's knee !

POCAHONTAS.

WEARIED arm and broken sword
  Wage in vain the desperate fight :
Round him press a countless horde,
  He is but a single knight.
Hark ! a cry of triumph shrill
  Through the wilderness resounds,
  As, with twenty bleeding wounds,
Sinks the warrior, fighting still.

Now they heap the fatal pyre,
   And the torch of death they light;
Ah ! 'tis hard to die of fire !
   Who will shield the captive knight?
Round the stake with fiendish cry
   Wheel and dance the savage crowd,
   Cold the victim's mien, and proud,
And his breast is bared to die.

Who will shield the fearless heart ?
   Who avert the murderous blade?
From the throng, with sudden start,
   See there springs an Indian maid.
Quick she stands before the knight :
   " Loose the chain, unbind the ring ;
   I am daughter of the king,
And I claim the Indian right !"

Dauntlessly aside she flings
   Lifted axe and thirsty knife ;
Fondly to his heart she clings,
   And her bosom guards his life !
In the woods of Powhattan,
   Still 'tis told by Indian fires,
   How a daughter of their sires
Saved the captive Englishman.

FROM POCAHONTAS.

RETURNING from the cruel fight
How pale and faint appears my knight!
He sees me anxious at his side;
"Why seek, my love, your wounds to hide?
Or deem your English girl afraid
To emulate the Indian maid?"

Be mine my husband's grief to cheer,
In peril to be ever near;
Whate'er of ill or woe betide,
To bear it clinging at his side;
The poisoned stroke of fate to ward,
His bosom with my own to guard:
Ah! could it spare a pang to his,
It could not know a purer bliss!
'Twould gladden as it felt the smart,
And thank the hand that flung the dart!

THE LEGEND OF ST. SOPHIA OF KIOFF.

AN EPIC POEM, IN TWENTY BOOKS.

I.

The Poet describes the city and spelling of Kiow, Kioff, or Kiova.

A THOUSAND years ago, or more,
   A city filled with burghers stout,
   And girt with ramparts round about,
Stood on the rocky Dnieper shore.
In armour bright, by day and night,
   The sentries they paced to and fro.
Well guarded and walled was this town, and called
   By different names, I'd have you to know;

For if you looks in the g'ography books,
In those dictionaries the name it varies,
And they write it off Kieff or Kioff,
    Kiova or Kiow.

II.

Thus guarded without by wall and redoubt,
 Kiova within was a place of renown,
With more advantages than in those dark ages
 Were commonly known to belong to a town.
There were places and squares, and each year four fairs,
And regular aldermen and regular lord mayors ;
And streets, and alleys, and a bishop's palace ;
And a church with clocks for the orthodox—
With clocks and with spires, as religion desires ;
And beadles to whip the bad little boys
Over their poor little corduroys,
In service-time, when they *didn't* make a noise ;
And a chapter and dean, and a cathedral-green
With ancient trees, underneath whose shades
Wandered nice young nursery-maids.
Ding-dong, ding-dong, ding-ding-a-ring-ding,
The bells they made a merry merry ring,
From the tall tall steeple ; and all the people
(Except the Jews) came and filled the pews—
   Poles, Russians and Germans,
   To hear the sermons
Which HYACINTH preached to those Germans and
    Poles
   For the safety of their souls.

Its buildings, public works, and ordinances, religious and civil.

The poet shows how a certain priest dwelt at Kioff, a godly clergyman, and one that preached rare good sermons.

III.

A worthy priest he was and a stout—
 You've seldom looked on such a one ;
For, though he fasted thrice in a week,
Yet nevertheless his skin was sleek ;
His waist it spanned two yards about,
 And he weighed a score of stone.

How this priest was short and fat of body

IV.

And like unto
he author of
"Plymley's
Letters."

A worthy priest for fasting and prayer
   And mortification most deserving,
And as for preaching beyond compare :
He'd exert his powers for three or four hours
With greater pith than Sydney Smith
   Or the Reverend Edward Irving.

V.

Of what convent
he was prior,
and when the
convent was
built.

He was the prior of Saint Sophia
   (A Cockney rhyme, but no better I know)—
Of St. Sophia, that Church in Kiow,
   Built by missionaries I can't tell when ;
Who by their discussions converted the Russians,
   And made them Christian men.

VI.

Of Saint Sophia
of Kioff; and
how her statue
miraculously
travelled
thither.

Sainted Sophia (so the legend vows)
With special favour did regard this house;
   And to uphold her converts' new devotion
Her statue (needing but her legs for *her* ship)
   Walks of itself across the German Ocean ;
      And of a sudden perches
      In this the best of churches,
Whither all Kiovites come and pay it grateful worship.

VII.

And how Kioff
should have
been a happy
city ; but that

Thus with her patron-saints and pious preachers
   Recorded here in catalogue precise,
A goodly city, worthy magistrates,
You would have thought in all the Russian states
The citizens the happiest of all creatures,—
   The town itself a perfect Paradise.

VIII.

No, alas ! this well-built city
  Was in a perpetual fidget ;
For the Tartars, without pity,
  Did remorselessly besiege it.

Certain wicked
Cossacks did
besiege it,

Tartars fierce, with swords and sabres,
  Huns and Turks, and such as these,
Envied much their peaceful neighbours
  By the blue Borysthenes.

Down they came, these ruthless Russians,
  From their steppes, and woods, and fens,
For to levy contributions
  On the peaceful citizens.

Murdering the
citizens,

Winter, Summer, Spring, and Autumn,
  Down they came to peaceful Kioff,
Killed the burghers when they caught 'em,
  If their lives they would not buy off.

Till the city, quite confounded
  By the ravages they made,
Humbly with their chief compounded,
  And a yearly tribute paid.

Until they
agreed to pay a
tribute yearly.

Which (because their courage lax was)
  They discharged while they were able :
Tolerated thus the tax was,
  Till it grew intolerable,

How they paid
the tribute, and
then suddenly
refused it,

And the Calmuc envoy sent,
  As before to take their dues all,
Got, to his astonishment,
  A unanimous refusal !

To the wonder
of the Cossack
envoy.

" Men of Kioff ! " thus courageous
  Did the stout lord-mayor harangue them,
" Wherefore pay these sneaking wages
  To the hectoring Russians ? hang them !

Of a mighty gal-
lant speech

That the lord-
mayor made,
> " Hark !   I hear the awful cry of
>   Our forefathers in their graves ;
> " ' Fight, ye citizens of Kioff !
>   Kioff was not made for slaves.'

Exhorting the
burghers to pay
no longer.
> " All too long have ye betrayed her ;
>   Rouse, ye men and aldermen,
> Send the insolent invader—
>   Send him starving back again."

IX.

Of their thanks
and heroic
resolves.
He spoke and he sat down ; the people of the town,
    Who were fired with a brave emulation,
Now rose with one accord, and voted thanks unto the lord-
    Mayor for his oration :

They dismiss the
envoy, and set
about drilling.
The envoy they dismissed, never placing in his fist
    So much as a single shilling ;
And all with courage fired, as his lordship he desired,
    At once set about their drilling.

Of the City
guard : viz.
militia,
dragoons, and
bombardiers,
and their com-
manders.
Then every city ward established a guard,
    Diurnal and nocturnal :
Militia volunteers, light dragoons, and bombardiers,
    With an alderman for colonel.

There was muster and roll-calls, and repairing city walls,
    And filling up of fosses :
Of the majors
and captains,
And the captains and the majors, so gallant and courageous,
    A-riding about on their hosses.

The fortifications
and artillery.
To be guarded at all hours they built themselves watch-towers,
    With every tower a man on ;

And surely and secure, each from out his embrasure,
    Looked down the iron cannon !

A battle-song was writ for the theatre, where it
    Was sung with vast enérgy
And rapturous applause ; and besides, the public cause
    Was supported by the clergy.

Of the conduct of the actors and the clergy.

The pretty ladies'-maids were pinning of cockades,
    And tying on of sashes ;
And dropping gentle tears, while their lovers bluster'd
      fierce
    About gun-shot and gashes ;

The ladies took the hint, and all day were scraping lint,
    As became their softer genders ;
And got bandages and beds for the limbs and for the
      heads
    Of the city's brave defenders.

Of the ladies

The men, both young and old, felt resolute and bold,
    And panted hot for glory ;
Even the tailors 'gan to brag, and embroidered on their
      flag,
      "AUT WINCERE AUT MORI."

And, finally, of the taylors.

X.

Seeing the city's resolute condition,
    The Cossack chief, too cunning to despise it,
Said to himself, " Not having ammunition
Wherewith to batter the place in proper form,
Some of these nights I'll carry it by storm,
    And sudden escalade it or surprise it.

Of the Cossack chief,—his stratagem ;

" Let's see, however, if the cits stand firmish."
    He rode up to the city gates ; for answers,
Out rushed an eager troop of the town *élite,*
And straightway did begin a gallant skirmish :
The Cossack hereupon did sound retreat,
    Leaving the victory with the city lancers.

And the burghers' sillie victorie.

What prisoners
they took,

They took two prisoners and as many horses,
　　And the whole town grew quickly so elate
With this small victory of their virgin forces,
That they did deem their privates and commanders
So many Cæsars, Pompeys, Alexanders,
　　Napoleons, or Fredericks the Great.

And how con-
ceited they were

And puffing with inordinate conceit
　　They utterly despised these Cossack thieves ;
And thought the ruffians easier to beat
Than porters carpets think, or ushers boys.
Meanwhile, a sly spectator of their joys,
　　The Cossack captain giggled in his sleeves.

Of the Cossack
chief,—his
orders ;

" Whene'er you meet yon stupid city hogs "
　　(He bade his troops precise this order keep),
" Don't stand a moment—run away, you dogs ! "
'Twas done ; and when they met the town battalions,
The Cossacks, as if frightened at their valiance,
　　Turned tail, and bolted like so many sheep.

And how he
feigned a retreat.

They fled, obedient to their captain's order :
　　And now this bloodless siege a month had lasted,
When, viewing the country round, the city warder
　　(Who, like a faithful weathercock, did perch
Upon the steeple of St. Sophy's church),
　　Sudden his trumpet took, and a mighty blast he
　　　　blasted.

The warder pro-
clayms the Cos-
sacks' retreat,
and the citie
greatly rejoyces.

His voice it might be heard through all the streets
　　(He was a warder wondrous strong in lung),
" Victory, victory ! the foe retreats ! "
" The foe retreats ! " each cries to each he meets ;
" The foe retreats ! " each in his turn repeats.
　　Gods ! how the guns did roar, and how the joy-bells
　　　　rung !

Arming in haste his gallant city lancers,
　　The mayor, to learn if true the news might be,
A league or two out issued with his prancers.

The Cossacks (something had given their courage a
   damper)
Hastened their flight, and 'gan like mad to scamper;
   Blessed be all the saints, Kiova town was free!

XI.

Now, puffed with pride, the mayor grew vain,
Fought all his battles o'er again;
And thrice he routed all his foes, and thrice he slew the
   slain.
'Tis true he might amuse himself thus,
And not be very murderous;
For as of those who to death were done
The number was exactly *none*,
His lordship, in his soul's elation,
Did take a bloodless recreation—
Going home again, he did ordain
A very splendid cold collation
For the magistrates and the corporation;
Likewise a grand illumination
For the amusement of the nation.
That night the theatres were free,
The conduits they ran Malvoisie;
Each house that night did beam with light
And sound with mirth and jollity:
But shame, O shame! not a soul in the town,
Now the city was safe and the Cossacks flown,
Ever thought of the bountiful saint by whose care
   The town had been rid of these terrible Turks—
Said even a prayer to that patroness fair
   For these her wondrous works!
Lord Hyacinth waited, the meekest of priors—
He waited at church with the rest of his friars;
He went there at noon and he waited till ten,
Expecting in vain the lord-mayor and his men.
   He waited and waited from mid-day to dark;
But in vain—you might search through the whole of
   the church,

The manner of the citie's rejoycings,

And its impiety.

How the priest, Hyacinth, waited at church, and nobody came thither.

21.   H

Not a layman, alas ! to the city's disgrace,
From mid-day to dark showed his nose in the place.
The pew-woman, organist, beadle, and clerk,
Kept away from their work, and were dancing like
    mad
Away in the streets with the other mad people,
Not thinking to pray, but to guzzle and tipple
Wherever the drink might be had.

XII.

How he went
forth to bid
them to prayer.

Amidst this din and revelry throughout the city roaring,
The silver moon rose silently, and high in heaven
    soaring ;
Prior Hyacinth was fervently upon his knees adoring :
" Towards my precious patroness this conduct sure
    unfair is ;
I cannot think, I must confess, what keeps the dignitaries
And our good mayor away, unless some business them
    contraries."

He puts his long white mantle on, and forth the prior
    sallies—
(His pious thoughts were bent upon good deeds and not
    on malice) :
Heavens ! how the banquet lights they shone about the
    mayor's palace !

How the grooms
and lackeys
jeered him.

About the hall the scullions ran with meats both fresh
    and potted ;
The pages came with cup and can, all for the guests
    allotted ;
Ah, how they jeered that good fat man as up the stairs
    he trotted !

He entered in the ante-rooms where sat the mayor's
    court in ;
He found a pack of drunken grooms a-dicing and
    a-sporting ;
The horrid wine and 'bacco fumes, they set the prior
    a-snorting !

The prior thought he'd speak about their sins .before he
    went hence,
And lustily began to shout of sin and of repentance ;
The rogues, they kicked the prior out before he'd done a
    sentence !

And having got no portion small of buffeting and tussling,
At last he reached the banquet-hall, where sat the mayor
    a-guzzling,
And by his side his lady tall dressed out in white sprig
    muslin.
Around the table in a ring the guests were drinking
    heavy ;
They drunk the church, and drunk the king, and the
    army and the navy ;
In fact they'd toasted everything.   The prior said, " God
    save ye !"

And the mayor,
mayoress, and
aldermen, being
tipsie, refused to
go to church.

The mayor cried, " Bring a silver cup—there's one upon
    the buffet ;
And, Prior, have the venison up—it's capital *réchauffé.*
And so, Sir Priest, you've come to sup? And pray you,
    how's Saint Sophy ? "
The prior's face quite red was grown with horror and
    with anger ;
He flung the proffered goblet down—it made a hideous
    clangour ;
And 'gan a-preaching with a frown—he was a fierce
    haranguer.

He tried the mayor and aldermen—they all set up
    a jeering :
He tried the common-councilmen—they too began
    a-sneering :
He turned towards the may'ress then, and hoped to get
    a hearing.
He knelt and seized her dinner-dress, made of the muslin
    snowy,
" To church, to church, my sweet mistress !" he cried ;
    " the way I'll show ye."
Alas, the lady-mayoress fell back as drunk as Chloe !

XIII.

How the prior
went back alone,

Out from this dissolute and drunken court
   Went the good prior, his eyes with weeping dim:
He tried the people of a meaner sort—
   They too, alas, were bent upon their sport,
     And not a single soul would follow him!
But all were swigging schnapps and guzzling beer.

He found the cits, their daughters, sons, and spouses,
   Spending the live-long night in fierce carouses:
     Alas, unthinking of the danger near!
One or two sentinels the ramparts guarded,
   The rest were sharing in the general feast:
" God wot, our tipsy town is poorly warded;
   Sweet Saint Sophia help us!" cried the priest.

Alone he entered the cathedral gate,
   Careful he locked the mighty oaken door;
Within his company of monks did wait,
   A dozen poor old pious men—no more.
   Oh, but it grieved the gentle prior sore,
To think of those lost souls, given up to drink and fate!

And shut himself
into Saint
Sophia's chapel
with his
brethren.

The mighty outer gate well barred and fast,
   The poor old friars stirred their poor old bones,
   And pattering swiftly on the damp cold stones,
They through the solitary chancel passed.
The chancel walls looked black and dim and vast,
   And rendered, ghost-like, melancholy tones.

Onward the fathers sped, till coming nigh a
   Small iron gate, the which they entered quick at,
   They locked and double-locked the inner wicket
And stood within the chapel of Sophia.
Vain were it to describe this sainted place,
   Vain to describe that celebrated trophy,
   The venerable statue of Saint Sophy,
Which formed its chiefest ornament and grace.

Here the good prior, his personal griefs and sorrows
  In his extreme devotion quickly merging,
At once began to pray with voice sonorous;
The other friars joined in pious chorus,
  And passed the night in singing, praying, scourging,
  In honour of Sophia, that sweet virgin.

XIV.

Leaving thus the pious priest in
  Humble penitence and prayer,
And the greedy cits a-feasting,
  Let us to the walls repair.

The episode of
Sneezoff and
Katinka.

Walking by the sentry-boxes,
  Underneath the silver moon,
Lo! the sentry boldly cocks his—
  Boldly cocks his musketoon.

Sneezoff was his designation,
  Fair-haired boy, for ever pitied;
For to take his cruel station,
  He but now Katinka quitted.

Poor in purse were both, but rich in
  Tender love's delicious plenties;
She a damsel of the kitchen,
  He a haberdasher's 'prentice.

'Tinka, maiden tender-hearted,
  Was dissolved in tearful fits,
On that fatal night she parted
  From her darling, fair-haired Fritz.

Warm her soldier lad she wrapt in
  Comforter and muffettee;
Called him "general" and "captain,"
  Though a simple private he.

"On your bosom wear this plaster,
    'Twill defend you from the cold;
In your pipe smoke this canaster—
    Smuggled 'tis, my love, and old.

"All the night, my love, I'll miss you."
    Thus she spoke; and from the door
Fair-haired Sneezoff made his issue,
    To return, alas, no more.

He it is who calmly walks his
    Walk beneath the silver moon;
He it is who boldly cocks his
    Detonating musketoon.

He the bland canaster puffing,
    As upon his round he paces,
Sudden sees a ragamuffin
    Clambering swiftly up the glacis.

"Who goes there?" exclaims the sentry;
    "When the sun has once gone down
No one ever makes an entry
    Into this here fortified town!"

How the sentrie
Sneezoff was
surprised and
slayn.
Shouted thus the watchful Sneezoff;
    But, ere any one replied,
Wretched youth! he fired his piece off,
    Started, staggered, groaned, and died!

                            XV.

How the Cos-
sacks rushed in
suddenly and
took the citie.
Ah, full well might the sentinel cry, "Who goes there?"
But echo was frightened too much to declare.
Who goes there? who goes there?   Can any one swear
To the number of sands *sur les bords de la mer*,
Or the whiskers of D'Orsay count down to a hair?
As well might you tell of the sands the amount,
Or number each hair in each curl of the Count,

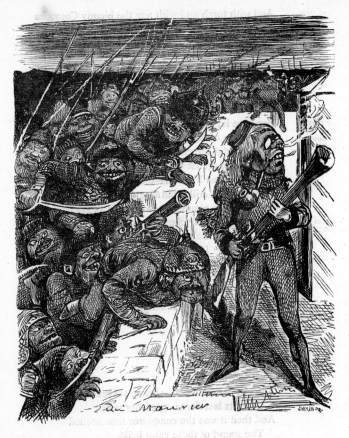

As ever proclaim the number and name
Of the hundreds and thousands that up the wall came !
Down, down the knaves poured with fire and with sword :
There were thieves from the Danube and rogues from Of the Cossack
    the Don ; troops,
There were Turks and Wallacks, and shouting Cossacks ;
Of all nations and regions, and tongues and religions—
Jew, Christian, idolater, Frank, Mussulman :
Ah, a horrible sight was Kioff that night !
The gates were all taken—no chance e'en of flight ;

And of their
manner of
burning, mur-
dering, and
ravishing.

And with torch and with axe the bloody Cossacks
Went hither and thither a-hunting in packs :
They slashed and they slew both Christian and Jew—
Women and children, they slaughtered them too.
Some, saving their throats, plunged into the moats,
Or the river—but oh, they had burned all the boats !

  *   *   *   *

How they
burned the whole
citie down, save
the church,

But here let us pause—for I can't pursue further
This scene of rack, ravishment, ruin, and murther.
Too well did the cunning old Cossack succeed !
His plan of attack was successful indeed !
The night was his own—the town it was gone ;
'Twas a heap still a-burning of timber and stone.
One building alone had escaped from the fires,

Whereof the bells
began to ring.

Saint Sophy's fair church, with its steeples and spires.
   Calm, stately, and white,
    It stood in the light ;
And as if 'twould defy all the conqueror's power,—
   As if nought had occurred,
    Might clearly be heard
The chimes ringing soberly every half-hour !

XVI.

The city was defunct—silence succeeded
  Unto its last fierce agonising yells ;
And then it was the conqueror first heeded
  The sound of these calm bells.

How the Cossack
chief bade them
burn the church
too.

Furious towards his aides-de-camp he turns,
  And (speaking as if Byron's works he knew)
" Villains ! " he fiercely cries, " the city burns,
  Why not the temple too ?
Burn me yon church, and murder all within ! "

How they
stormed it ;
and of Hyacinth,
his anger
thereat,

  The Cossacks thundered at the outer door ;
And Father Hyacinth, who heard the din,
(And thought himself and brethren in distress,
Deserted by their lady patroness)
  Did to her statue turn, and thus his woes outpour.

XVII.

" And is it thus, O falsest of the saints,
  Thou hearest our complaints ?
Tell me, did ever my attachment falter
  To serve thy altar ?
Was not thy name, ere ever I did sleep,
  The last upon my lip ?
Was not thy name the very first that broke
  From me when I awoke ?
Have I not tried with fasting, flogging, penance,
  And mortified counténance
For to find favour, Sophy, in thy sight ?
  And lo ! this night,
Forgetful of my prayers and thine own promise,
  Thou turnest from us ;
Lettest the heathen enter in our city,
  And, without pity,
Murder our burghers, seize upon their spouses,
  Burn down their houses !
Is such a breach of faith to be endured?
  See what a lurid
Light from the insolent invader's torches
  Shines on your porches !
E'en now, with thundering battering-ram and hammer
  And hideous clamour,
With axemen, swordsmen, pikemen, billmen, bowmen,
  The conquering foemen,
O Sophy ! beat your gate about your ears,
  Alas ! and here's
A humble company of pious men,
  Like muttons in a pen,
Whose souls shall quickly from their bodies be thrusted,
  Because in you they trusted.
Do you not know the Calmuc chief's desires—
  KILL ALL THE FRIARS !
And you, of all the saints most false and fickle,
  Leave us in this abominable pickle."

His prayer to
the Saint Sophia.

The statue sud-
denlie speaks;

" RASH HYACINTHUS ! "
     (Here, to the astonishment of all her backers,
Saint Sophy, opening wide her wooden jaws,
     Like to a pair of German walnut-crackers,
Began), " I did not think you had been thus,—
O monk of little faith !   Is it because
A rascal scum of filthy Cossack heathen
Besiege our town, that you distrust in *me*, then ?
Think'st thou that I, who in a former day
Did walk across the sea of Marmora
(Not mentioning, for shortness, other seas),—
That I, who skimmed the broad Borysthenes,
Without so much as wetting of my toes,
Am frightened at a set of men like *those?*
I have a mind to leave you to your fate :
Such cowardice as this my scorn inspires."

But is inter-
rupted by the
breaking in of
the Cossacks.

Saint Sophy was here
     Cut short in her words,—
For at this very moment in tumbled the gate,
     And with a wild cheer,
          And a clashing of swords,
     Swift through the church porches,
     With a waving of torches,
     And a shriek and a yell
     Like the devils of hell,
     With pike and with axe
     In rushed the Cossacks,—
In   rushed   the   Cossacks,   crying,   " MURDER   THE
     FRIARS ! "

Of Hyacinth, his
courageous
address ;

Ah ! what a thrill felt Hyacinth,
     When he heard that villanous shout Calmuc !
Now, thought he, my trial beginneth ;
     Saints, O give me courage and pluck !
" Courage, boys, 'tis useless to funk ! "
     Thus unto the friars he began :
" Never let it be said that a monk
     Is not likewise a gentleman.

Though the patron saint of the church,
　　Spite of all that we've done and we've pray'd,
Leaves us wickedly here in the lurch,
　　Hang it, gentlemen, who's afraid?"

As thus the gallant Hyacinthus spoke,　　　　*And preparation*
　　He, with an air as easy and as free as　　　　*for dying.*
If the quick-coming murder were a joke,
Folded his robes around his sides, and took
Place under sainted Sophy's legs of oak,
　　Like Cæsar at the statue of Pompeius.
The monks no leisure had about to look
(Each being absorbed in his particular case),
Else had they seen with what celestial grace
A wooden smile stole o'er the saint's mahogany face.

" Well done, well done, Hyacinthus, my son !"　　*Saint Sophia, her*
　　Thus spoke the sainted statue.　　　　　　　*speech.*
" Though you doubted me in the hour of need,
And spoke of me very rude indeed,
You deserve good luck for showing such pluck,
　　And I won't be angry at you."

　　The monks by-standing, one and all,　　　　*She gets on the*
　　　　Of this wondrous scene beholders,　　　　*prior's shoulder*
　　　　To this kind promise listened content,　　　*straddleback.*
　　And couldn't contain their astonishment,
　　When Saint Sophia moved and went
　　Down from her wooden pedestal,
　　　And twisted her legs, sure as eggs is eggs,
　　　　Round Hyacinthus's shoulders !

" Ho ! forwards," cries Sophy, "there's no time for　*And bids him*
　　waiting,　　　　　　　　　　　　　　　　　　*run.*
The Cossacks are breaking the very last gate in :
See, the glare of their torches shines red through the
　　grating;
　　We've still the back door, and two minutes or more.
Now, boys, now or never, we must make for the river,
　　For we only are safe on the opposite shore.

Run swiftly to-day, lads, if ever you ran,—
Put out your best leg, Hyacinthus, my man ;
And I'll lay five to two that you carry us through,
   Only scamper as fast as you can."

XVIII.

He runneth,   Away went the priest through the little back door,
And light on his shoulders the image he bore :
   The honest old priest was not punished the least,
Though the image was eight feet, and he measured four.
Away went the prior, and the monks at his tail
Went snorting, and puffing, and panting full sail ;
   And just as the last at the back door had passed,
In furious hunt behold at the front
The Tartars so fierce, with their terrible cheers ;
With axes, and halberts, and muskets, and spears,
With torches a-flaming the chapel now came in.
They tore up the mass-book, they stamped on the psalter,
They pulled the gold crucifix down from the altar ;
The vestments they burned with their blasphemous
   fires,
And many cried, " Curse on them ! where are the friars ? "
When loaded with plunder, yet seeking for more,
One chanced to fling open the little back door,
Spied out the friars' white robes and long shadows
In the moon, scampering over the meadows,
And stopped the Cossacks in the midst of their arsons,
And the Tartars By crying out lustily, " THERE GO THE PARSONS ! "
after him.
With a whoop and a yell, and a scream and a shout,
At once the whole murderous body turned out ;
And swift as the hawk pounces down on the pigeon,
Pursued the poor short-winded men of religion.

How the friars When the sound of that cheering came to the monks'
sweated,   hearing,
   O heaven ! how the poor fellows panted and blew !
At fighting not cunning, unaccustomed to running,
   When the Tartars came up, what the deuce should
     they do ?

"They'll make us all martyrs, those blood-thirsty Tartars!"
  Quoth fat Father Peter to fat Father Hugh.
The shouts they came clearer, the foe they drew nearer;
  Oh, how the bolts whistled, and how the lights shone!
" I cannot get further, this running is murther;
  Come carry me, some one!" cried big Father John.
And even the statue grew frightened: " Od rat you!"
  It cried, " Mr. Prior, I wish you'd get on!"
On tugged the good friar, but nigher and nigher
Appeared the fierce Russians, with sword and with fire.
On tugged the good prior at Saint Sophy's desire,—
A scramble through bramble, through mud, and through
      mire,
The swift arrows' whizziness causing a dizziness.
Nigh done his business, fit to expire,
Father Hyacinth tugged, and the monks they tugged
      after:
The foemen pursued with a horrible laughter,
And hurl'd their long spears round the poor brethren's   And the pur-
      ears   suers fixed
So true, that next day in the coat of each priest,   arrows into
Though never a wound was given, there were found   their tayls.
      A dozen arrows at least.

      Now the chase seemed at its worst,   How, at the last
      Prior and monks were fit to burst;   gasp,
      Scarce you knew the which was first,
        Or pursuers or pursued;
      When the statue, by Heaven's grace,
      Suddenly did change the face
      Of this interesting race,
        As a saint, sure, only could.

For as the jockey who at Epsom rides,
  When that his steed is spent and punished sore,
Diggeth his heels into the courser's sides,
  And thereby makes him run one or two furlongs more;
  Even thus, betwixt the eighth rib and the ninth,
The saint rebuked the prior, that weary creeper;
  Fresh strength into his limbs her kicks imparted,
  One bound he made, as gay as when he started.

The friars won, and jumped into Borysthenes fluvius.

Yes, with his brethren clinging at his cloak,
The statue on his shoulders—fit to choke—
One most tremendous bound made Hyacinth,
And soused friars, statue, and all, slapdash into the
    Dnieper !

XIX.

And how the Russians saw

And when the Russians, in a fiery rank,
    Panting and fierce, drew up along the shore ;
    (For here the vain pursuing they forbore,
Nor cared they to surpass the river's bank,)
Then, looking from the rocks and rushes dank,
    A sight they witnessed never seen before,
And which, with its accompaniments glorious,
Is writ i' the golden book, or *liber aureus*.

Plump in the Dnieper flounced the friar and friends,—
  They dangling round his neck, he fit to choke,
  When suddenly his most miraculous cloak
Over the billowy waves itself extends,
Down from his shoulders quietly descends
  The venerable Sophy's statue of oak ;
Which, sitting down upon the cloak so ample,
Bids all the brethren follow its example !

The statue get off Hyacinth his back, and sit down with the friars on Hyacinth his cloak.

Each at her bidding sat, and sat at ease ;
  The statue 'gan a gracious conversation,
  And (waving to the foe a salutation)
Sail'd with her wondering happy protégés
Gaily adown the wide Borysthenes,
  Until they came unto some friendly nation.
And when the heathen had at length grown shy of
Their conquest, she one day came back again to Kioff.

How in this manner of boat they sayled away.

XX.

THINK NOT, O READER, THAT WE'RE LAUGHING AT
  YOU ;
YOU MAY GO TO KIOFF NOW AND SEE THE STATUE !

Finis, or the end.

TITMARSH'S CARMEN LILLIENSE.

LILLE, *Sept.* 2, 1843.

My heart is weary, my peace is gone,
How shall I e'er my woes reveal?
I have no money, I lie in pawn,
A stranger in the town of Lille.

I.

WITH twenty pounds but three weeks since
From Paris forth did Titmarsh wheel,
I thought myself as rich a prince
As beggar poor I'm now at Lille.

Confiding in my ample means—
    In troth, I was a happy chiel !
I passed the gates of Valenciennes,
    I never thought to come by Lille.

I never thought my twenty pounds
    Some rascal knave would dare to steal ;
I gaily passed the Belgic bounds
    At Quiévrain, twenty miles from Lille.

To Antwerp town I hastened post,
    And as I took my evening meal
I felt my pouch,—my purse was lost,
    O Heaven !   Why came I not by Lille ?

I straightway called for ink and pen,
    To grandmamma I made appeal ;
Meanwhile a loan of guineas ten
    I borrowed from a friend so leal.

I got the cash from grandmamma
    (Her gentle heart my woes could feel,)
But where I went, and what I saw,
    What matters ?   Here I am at Lille.

My heart is weary, my peace is gone,
    How shall I e'er my woes reveal ?
I have no cash, I lie in pawn,
    A stranger in the town of Lille.

II.

To stealing I can never come,
    To pawn my watch I'm too genteel :
Besides, I left my watch at home—
    How could I pawn it then at Lille ?

" *La note,*" at times the guests will say.
    I turn as white as cold boil'd veal ;
I turn and look another way,
    I dare not ask the bill at Lille.

I

I dare not to the landlord say,
   "Good sir, I cannot pay your bill;"
He thinks I am a Lord Anglais,
   And is quite proud I stay at Lille.

He thinks I am a Lord Anglais,
   Like Rothschild or Sir Robert Peel,
And so he serves me every day
   The best of meat and drink in Lille.

Yet when he looks me in the face
   I blush as red as cochineal;
And think, did he but know my case,
   How changed he'd be, my host of Lille.

My heart is weary, my peace is gone,
   How shall I e'er my woes reveal?
I have no money, I lie in pawn,
   A stranger in the town of Lille.

III.

The sun bursts out in furious blaze,
   I perspirate from head to heel;
I'd like to hire a one-horse chaise—
   How can I, without cash at Lille?

I pass in sunshine burning hot
   By cafés where in beer they deal;
I think how pleasant were a pot,
   A frothing pot of beer of Lille!

What is yon house with walls so thick,
   All girt around with guard and grille?
O gracious gods! it makes me sick,
   It is the *prison-house* of Lille!

O cursed prison strong and barred,
   It does my very blood congeal!

I tremble as I pass the guard,
  And quit that ugly part of Lille.

The church-door beggar whines and prays,
  I turn away at his appeal :
Ah, church-door beggar ! go thy ways !
  You're not the poorest man in Lille.

My heart is weary, my peace is gone,
  How shall I e'er my woes reveal ?
I have no money, I lie in pawn,
  A stranger in the town of Lille.

IV.

Say, shall I to yon Flemish church,
  And at a Popish altar kneel ?
O, do not leave me in the lurch,—
  I'll cry, ye patron-saints of Lille !

Ye virgins dressed in satin hoops,
  Ye martyrs slain for mortal weal,
Look kindly down ! before you stoops
  The miserablest man in Lille.

And lo ! as I beheld with awe
  A pictured saint (I swear 'tis real),
It smiled, and turned to grandmamma !—
  It did ! and I had hope in Lille !

'Twas five o'clock, and I could eat,
  Although I could not pay my meal :
I hasten back into the street
  Where lies my inn, the best in Lille.

What see I on my table stand,—
  A letter with a well-known seal ?
'Tis grandmamma's ! I know her hand,—
  " To Mr. M. A. Titmarsh, Lille."

I feel a choking in my throat,
    I pant and stagger, faint and reel !
It is—it is—a ten-pound note,
    And I'm no more in pawn at Lille !

[He goes off by the diligence that evening, and is restored to the bosom of his
happy family.]

JEAMES OF BUCKLEY SQUARE.

A HELIGY.

COME all ye gents vot cleans the plate,
  Come all ye ladies maids so fair—
Vile I a story vill relate
  Of cruel Jeames of Buckley Square.
A tighter lad, it is confest,
  Neer valked with powder in his air,
Or vore a nosegay in his breast,
  Than andsum Jeames of Buckley Square.

O Evns ! it vas the best of sights,
  Behind his Master's coach and pair,
To see our Jeames in red plush tights,
  A driving hoff from Buckley Square.
He vel became his hagwilletts,
  He cocked his at with *such* a hair ;
His calves and viskers *vas* such pets,
  That hall loved Jeames of Buckley Square.

He pleased the hup-stairs folks as vell,
  And o ! I vithered vith despair,
Missis *vould* ring the parler bell,
  And call up Jeames in Buckley Square.
Both beer and sperrits he abhord,
  (Sperrits and beer I can't a bear,)
You would have thought he vas a lord
  Down in our All in Buckley Square.

Last year he visper'd, " Mary Ann,
  Ven I've an under'd pound to spare,
To take a public is my plan,
  And leave this hojous Buckley Square."

O how my gentle heart did bound,
　　To think that I his name should bear!
"Dear Jeames," says I, "I've twenty pound,"
　　And gev them him in Buckley Square.

Our master vas a City gent,
　　His name's in railroads everywhere,
And lord, vot lots of letters vent
　　Betwigst his brokers and Buckley Square:
My Jeames it was the letters took,
　　And read them all, (I think it's fair,)
And took a leaf from Master's book,
　　As *hothers* do in Buckley Square.

Encouraged with my twenty pound,
　　Of which poor *I* was unavare,
He wrote the Companies all round,
　　And signed hisself from Buckley Square.
And how John Porter used to grin,
　　As day by day, share after share,
Came railvay letters pouring in,
　　" J. Plush, Esquire, in Buckley Square."

Our servants' All was in a rage—
　　Scrip, stock, curves, gradients, bull and bear
Vith butler, coachman, groom and page,
　　Vas all the talk in Buckley Square.
But O! imagine vot I felt
　　Last Vensday veek as ever were;
I gits a letter, which I spelt
　　" Miss M. A. Hoggins, Buckley Square."

He sent me back my money true—
　　He sent me back my lock of air,
And said, " My dear, I bid ajew
　　To Mary Hann and Buckley Square.
Think not to marry, foolish Hann,
　　With people who your betters are;
James Plush is now a gentleman,
　　And you—a cook in Buckley Square.

" I've thirty thousand guineas won,
   In six short months, by genus rare ;
You little thought what Jeames was on,
   Poor Mary Hann, in Buckley Square.
I've thirty thousand guineas net,
   Powder and plush I scorn to vear ;
And so, Miss Mary Hann, forget
   For hever Jeames of Buckley Square."

LINES UPON MY SISTER'S PORTRAIT.

BY THE LORD SOUTHDOWN.

THE castle towers of Bareacres are fair upon the lea,
Where the cliffs of bonny Diddlesex rise up from out the sea :
I stood upon the donjon keep and view'd the country o'er,
I saw the lands of Bareacres for fifty miles or more.
I stood upon the donjon keep—it is a sacred place,—
Where floated for eight hundred years the banner of my race ;
Argent, a dexter sinople, and gules an azure field :
There ne'er was nobler cognizance on knightly warrior's
    shield.

The first time England saw the shield 'twas round a Norman
    neck,
On board a ship from Valery, King William was on deck.
A Norman lance the colours wore, in Hastings' fatal fray—
St. Willibald for Bareacres ! 'twas double gules that day !
O Heaven and sweet St. Willibald ! in many a battle since
A loyal-hearted Bareacres has ridden by his Prince !
At Acre with Plantagenet, with Edward at Poictiers,
The pennon of the Bareacres was foremost on the spears !

'Twas pleasant in the battle-shock to hear our war-cry
    ringing :
O grant me, sweet St. Willibald, to listen to such singing !
Three hundred steel-clad gentlemen, we drove the foe
    before us,
And thirty score of British bows kept twanging to the
    chorus !
O knights, my noble ancestors ! and shall I never hear
St. Willibald for Bareacres through battle ringing clear ?
I'd cut me off this strong right hand a single hour to ride,
And strike a blow for Bareacres, my fathers, at your side !
Dash down, dash down, yon mandolin, beloved sister mine !

Those blushing lips may never sing the glories of our line :
Our ancient castles echo to the clumsy feet of churls,
The spinning-jenny houses in the mansion of our Earls.
Sing not, sing not, my Angeline ! in days so base and vile,
'Twere sinful to be happy, 'twere sacrilege to smile.
I'll hie me to my lonely hall, and by its cheerless hob
I'll muse on other days, and wish—and wish I were—A SNOB.

*LITTLE BILLEE.**

Air—" Il y avait un petit navire."

THERE were three sailors of Bristol city
Who took a boat and went to sea.
But first with beef and captain's biscuits
And pickled pork they loaded she.

* As different versions of this popular song have been set to music and
sung, no apology is needed for the insertion in these pages of what is considered to be the correct version.

There was gorging Jack and guzzling Jimmy,
And the youngest he was little Billee.
Now when they got as far as the Equator
They'd nothing left but one split pea.

Says gorging Jack to guzzling Jimmy,
" I am extremely hungaree."
To gorging Jack says guzzling Jimmy,
" We've nothing left, us must eat we."

Says gorging Jack to guzzling Jimmy,
" With one another we shouldn't agree !
There's little Bill, he's young and tender,
We're old and tough, so let's eat he.

" Oh ! Billy, we're going to kill and eat **you**,
So undo the button of your chemie."
When Bill received this information
He used his pocket handkerchie.

" First let me say my catechism,
Which my poor mamy taught to me."
" Make haste, make haste," says guzzling Jimmy,
While Jack pulled out his snickersnee.

So Billy went up to the main-top gallant mast,
And down he fell on his bended knee.
He scarce had come to the twelfth commandment
When up he jumps.   " There's land I see :

" Jerusalem and Madagascar,
And North and South Amerikee :
There's the British flag a riding at anchor,
With Admiral Napier, K.C.B."

So when they got aboard of the Admiral's
He hanged fat Jack and flogged Jimmee ;
But as for little Bill he made him
The Captain of a Seventy-three.

THE END OF THE PLAY.

THE play is done ; the curtain drops,
    Slow falling to the prompter's bell :
A moment yet the actor stops,
    And looks around, to say farewell.
It is an irksome word and task ;
    And, when he's laughed and said his say,
He shows, as he removes the mask,
    A face that's anything but gay.

One word, ere yet the evening ends,
    Let's close it with a parting rhyme,
And pledge a hand to all young friends,
    As fits the merry Christmas time.*
On life's wide scene you, too, have parts,
    That Fate ere long shall bid you play ;
Good night ! with honest gentle hearts
    A kindly greeting go alway!

Good night !—I'd say, the griefs, the joys,
    Just hinted in this mimic page,
The triumphs and defeats of boys,
    Are but repeated in our age.
I'd say, your woes were not less keen,
    Your hopes more vain, than those of men ;
Your pangs or pleasures of fifteen
    At forty-five played o'er again.

I'd say, we suffer and we strive,
    Not less nor more as men than boys ;
With grizzled beards at forty-five,
    As erst at twelve in corduroys.

---

  * These verses were printed at the end of a Christmas book (1848-9),
" Dr. Birch and his Young Friends."

And if, in time of sacred youth,
  We learned at home to love and pray,
Pray Heaven that early Love and Truth
  May never wholly pass away.

And in the world, as in the school,
  I'd say, how fate may change and shift;
The prize be sometimes with the fool,
  The race not always to the swift.
The strong may yield, the good may fall,
  The great man be a vulgar clown,
The knave be lifted over all,
  The kind cast pitilessly down.

Who knows the inscrutable design?
  Blessed be He who took and gave!
Why should your mother, Charles, not mine,
  Be weeping at her darling's grave? *
We bow to Heaven that will'd it so,
  That darkly rules the fate of all,
That sends the respite or the blow,
  That's free to give, or to recall.

This crowns his feast with wine and wit:
  Who brought him to that mirth and state?
His betters, see, below him sit,
  Or hunger hopeless at the gate.
Who bade the mud from Dives' wheel
  To spurn the rags of Lazarus?
Come, brother, in that dust we'll kneel,
  Confessing Heaven that ruled it thus.

So each shall mourn, in life's advance,
  Dear hopes, dear friends, untimely killed;
Shall grieve for many a forfeit chance,
  And longing passion unfulfilled.
Amen! whatever fate be sent,
  Pray God the heart may kindly glow,
Although the head with cares be bent,
  And whitened with the winter snow.

  * C. B. ob. 29th November, 1848, æt. 42.

Come wealth or want, come good or ill,
  Let young and old accept their part,
And bow before the Awful Will,
  And bear it with an honest heart,
Who misses or who wins the prize.
  Go, lose or conquer as you can ;
But if you fail, or if you rise,
  Be each, pray God, a gentleman.

A gentleman, or old or young !
  (Bear kindly with my humble lays) ;
The sacred chorus first was sung
  Upon the first of Christmas days :
The shepherds heard it overhead—
  The joyful angels raised it then :
Glory to Heaven on high, it said,
  And peace on earth to gentle men.

My song, save this, is little worth ;
  I lay the weary pen aside,
And wish you health, and love, and mirth,
  As fits the solemn Christmas-tide.
As fits the holy Christmas birth,
  Be this, good friends, our carol still—
Be peace on earth, be peace on earth,
  To men of gentle will.

VANITAS VANITATUM.

How spake of old the Royal Seer?
  (His text is one I love to treat on.)
This life of ours, he said, is sheer
  Mataiotes Mataioteton.

O Student of this gilded Book,
  Declare, while musing on its pages,
If truer words were ever spoke
  By ancient or by modern sages?

The various authors' names but note,*
  French, Spanish, English, Russians, Germans :
And in the volume polyglot,
  Sure you may read a hundred sermons !

---

* Between a page by Jules Janin, and a poem by the Turkish Ambassador,
in Madame de R——'s album, containing the autographs of kings, princes,
poets, marshals, musicians, diplomatists, statesmen, artists, and men of letters
of all nations.

What histories of life are here,
  More wild than all romancers' stories ;
What wondrous transformations queer,
  What homilies on human glories !

What theme for sorrow or for scorn !
  What chronicle of Fate's surprises—
Of adverse fortune nobly borne,
  Of chances, changes, ruins, rises !

Of thrones upset, and sceptres broke,
  How strange a record here is written !
Of honours, dealt as if in joke ;
  Of brave desert unkindly smitten.

How low men were, and how they rise
  How high they were, and how they tumble :
O vanity of vanities !
  O laughable, pathetic jumble !

Here between honest Janin's joke
  And his Turk Excellency's firman,
I write my name upon the book :
  I write my name—and end my sermon.

———————————

O Vanity of vanities !
  How wayward the decrees of Fate are ;
How very weak the very wise,
  How very small the very great are !

What mean these stale moralities,
  Sir Preacher, from your desk you mumble
Why rail against the great and wise,
  And tire us with your ceaseless grumble ?

Pray choose us out another text,
  O man morose and narrow-minded !
Come turn the page—I read the next,
  And then the next, and still I find it.

Read here how Wealth aside was thrust,
    And Folly set in place exalted ;
How Princes footed in the dust,
    While lackeys in the saddle vaulted.

Though thrice a thousand years are past
    Since David's son, the sad and splendid,
The weary King Ecclesiast,
    Upon his awful tablets penned it,—

Methinks the text is never stale,
    And life is every day renewing
Fresh comments on the old old tale
    Of Folly, Fortune, Glory, Ruin.

Hark to the Preacher, preaching still
    He lifts his voice and cries his sermon,
Here at St. Peter's on Cornhill,
    As yonder on the Mount of Hermon :

For you and me to heart to take
    (O dear beloved brother readers)
To-day as when the good King spake
    Beneath the solemn Syrian cedars.

LOVE-SONGS MADE EASY

LOVE-SONGS MADE EASY.

WHAT MAKES MY HEART TO THRILL AND GLOW?

THE MAYFAIR LOVE-SONG.

WINTER and summer, night and morn,
 I languish at this table dark ;
My office window has a corn-
 er looks into St. James's Park.
I hear the foot-guards' bugle-horn,
 Their tramp upon parade I mark ;
I am a gentleman forlorn,
 I am a Foreign-Office Clerk.

My toils, my pleasures, every one,
 I find are stale, and dull, and slow ;
And yesterday, when work was done,
 I felt myself so sad and low,

I could have seized a sentry's gun
   My wearied brains out out to blow.
What is it makes my blood to run?
   What makes·my heart to beat and glow?

My notes of hand are burnt, perhaps?
   Some one has paid my tailor's bill?
No : every morn the tailor raps ;
   My I O U's are extant still.
I still am prey of debt and dun ;
   My elder brother's stout and well.
What is it makes my blood to run?
   What makes my heart to glow and swell?

I know my chief's distrust and hate ;
   He says I'm lazy, and I shirk.
Ah ! had I genius like the late
   Right Honourable Edmund Burke !
My chance of all promotion's gone,
   I know it is,—he hates me so.
What is it makes my blood to run,
   And all my heart to swell and glow?

Why, why is all so bright and gay?
   There is no change, there is no cause ;
My office-time I found to-day
   Disgusting as it ever was.
At three, I went and tried the Clubs,
   And yawned and saunter'd to and fro ;
And now my heart jumps up and throbs,
   And all my soul is in a glow.

At half-past four I had the cab ;
   I drove as hard as I could go.
The London sky was dirty drab,
   And dirty brown the London snow.
And as I rattled in a cant-
   er down by dear old Bolton Row,
A something made my heart to pant,
   And caused my cheek to flush and glow.

What could it be that made me find
    Old Jawkins pleasant at the Club?
Why was it that I laughed and grinned
    At whist, although I lost the rub?
What was it made me drink like mad
    Thirteen small glasses of Curaçao?
That made my inmost heart so glad,
    And every fibre thrill and glow?

She's home again! she's home, she's home!
    Away all cares and griefs and pain;
I knew she would—she's back from Rome;
    She's home again! she's home again!
" The family's gone abroad," they said,
    September last—they told me so;
Since then my lonely heart is dead,
    My blood, I think 's forgot to flow.

She's home again! away all care!
    O fairest form the world can show!
O beaming eyes! O golden hair!
    O tender voice, that breathes so low!
O gentlest, softest, purest heart!
    O joy, O hope!—" My tiger, ho!"
Fitz-Clarence said; we saw him start—
    He galloped down to Bolton Row.

THE GHAZUL, OR ORIENTAL LOVE-SONG.

THE ROCKS.

I WAS a timid little antelope ;
My home was in the rocks, the lonely rocks.

I saw the hunters scouring on the plain ;
I lived among the rocks, the lonely rocks.

I was a-thirsty in the summer-heat ;
I ventured to the tents beneath the rocks.

Zuleikah brought me water from the well ;
Since then I have been faithless to the rocks.

I saw her face reflected in the well ;
Her camels since have marched into the rocks.

I look to see her image in the well ;
I only see my eyes, my own sad eyes.
My mother is alone among the rocks.

THE MERRY BARD.

ZULEIKAH! The young Agas in the bazaar are slim-waisted and wear yellow slippers. I am old and hideous. One of my eyes is out, and the hairs of my beard are mostly grey. Praise be to Allah! I am a merry bard.

There is a bird upon the terrace of the Emir's chief wife. Praise be to Allah! He has emeralds on his neck, and a ruby tail. I am a merry bard. He deafens me with his diabolical screaming.

There is a little brown bird in the basket-maker's cage. Praise be to Allah! He ravishes my soul in the moonlight. I am a merry bard.

The peacock is an Aga, but the little bird is a Bulbul.

I am a little brown Bulbul. Come and listen in the moonlight. Praise be to Allah! I am a merry bard.

THE CAIQUE.

YONDER to the kiosk, beside the creek,
Paddle the swift caïque.
Thou brawny oarsman with the sun-burnt cheek,
Quick ! for it soothes my heart to hear the Bulbul speak.

Ferry me quickly to the Asian shores,
Swift bending to your oars.

Beneath the melancholy sycamores,
Hark ! what a ravishing note the love-lorn Bulbul pours!

Behold, the boughs seem quivering with delight,
The stars themselves more bright,
As mid the waving branches out of sight
The Lover of the Rose sits singing through the night.

Under the boughs I sat and listened still,
I could not have my fill.
" How comes," I said, " such music to his bill ?
Tell me for whom he sings so beautiful a trill."

" Once I was dumb," then did the Bird disclose,
" But looked upon the Rose ;
And in the garden where the loved one grows,
I straightway did begin sweet music to compose."

"O bird of song, there's one in this caïque
The Rose would also seek,
So he might learn like you to love and speak."
Then answered me the bird of dusky beak,
"The Rose, the Rose of Love blushes on Leilah's cheek."

MY NORA.

BENEATH the gold acacia buds
My gentle Nora sits and broods,
Far, far away in Boston woods
   My gentle Nora !

I see the tear-drop in her e'e,
Her bosom's heaving tenderly ;
I know—I know she thinks of me,
   My darling Nora !

And where am I?   My love, whilst thou
Sitt'st sad beneath the acacia bough,
Where pearl's on neck, and wreath on brow,
   I stand, my Nora !

Mid carcanet and coronet,
Where joy-lamps shine and flowers are set—
Where England's chivalry are met,
   Behold me, Nora !

In this strange scene of revelry,
Amidst this gorgeous chivalry,
A form I saw was like to thee,
        My love—my Nora !

She paused amidst her converse glad ;
The lady saw that I was sad,
She pitied the poor lonely lad,—
        Dost love her, Nora ?

In sooth, she is a lovely dame,
A lip of red, and eye of flame,
And clustering golden locks, the same
        As thine, dear Nora !

Her glance is softer than the dawn's,
Her foot is lighter than the fawn's,
Her breast is whiter than the swan's,
        Or thine, my Nora !

Oh, gentle breast to pity me !
Oh, lovely Ladye Emily !
Till death—till death I'll think of thee—
        Of thee and Nora !

TO MARY.

I SEEM, in the midst of the crowd,
    The lightest of all ;
My laughter rings cheery and loud
    In banquet and ball.
My lip hath its smiles and its sneers,
    For all men to see ;
But my soul, and my truth, and my tears,
    Are for thee, are for thee !

Around me they flatter and fawn—
    The young and the old,

The fairest are ready to pawn
    Their hearts for my gold.
They sue me—I laugh as I spurn
    The slaves at my knee ;
But in faith and in fondness I turn
    Unto thee, unto thee !

SERENADE.

Now the toils of day are over,
   And the sun hath sunk to rest,
Seeking, like a fiery lover,
   The bosom of the blushing west—

The faithful night keeps watch and ward,
   Raising the moon her silver shield,
And summoning the stars to guard
   The slumbers of my fair Mathilde !

The faithful night !   Now all things lie
   Hid by her mantle dark and dim,
In pious hope I hither hie,
   And humbly chant mine evening hymn.

Thou art my prayer, my saint, my shrine !
   (For never holy pilgrim kneel'd
Or wept at feet more pure than thine),
   My virgin love, my sweet Mathilde !

FIVE GERMAN DITTIES

FIVE GERMAN DITTIES.

A TRAGIC STORY.

BY ADELBERT VON CHAMISSO.

"——'s war Einer, dem's zu Herzen gieng."

THERE lived a sage in days of yore,
And he a handsome pigtail wore ;
But wondered much and sorrowed more
Because it hung behind him.

He mused upon this curious case,
And swore he'd change the pigtail's place,
And have it hanging at his face,
    Not dangling there behind him.

Says he, " The mystery I've found,—
I'll turn me round,"—he turned him round ;
    But still it hung behind him.

Then round, and round, and out and in,
All day the puzzled sage did spin ;
In vain—it mattered not a pin,—
    The pigtail hung behind him.

And right, and left, and round about,
And up, and down, and in, and out,
He turned ; but still the pigtail stout
    Hung steadily behind him.

And though his efforts never slack,
And though he twist, and twirl, and tack,
Alas ! still faithful to his back
    The pigtail hangs behind him.

THE CHAPLET.

FROM UHLAND.

"Es pflückte Blümlein mannigfalt."

A LITTLE girl through field and wood
    Went plucking flowerets here and there,
When suddenly beside her stood
    A lady wondrous fair.

The lovely lady smiled, and laid
　A wreath upon the maiden's brow :
"Wear it ; 'twill blossom soon," she said,
　"Although 'tis leafless now."

The little maiden older grew
　And wandered forth of moonlight eves,
And sighed and loved as maids will do ;
　When, lo ! her wreath bore leaves.

Then was our maid a wife, and hung
　Upon a joyful bridegroom's bosom ;
When from the garland's leaves there sprung
　Fair store of blossom.

And presently a baby fair
　Upon her gentle breast she reared ;
When midst the wreath that bound her hair
　Rich golden fruit appeared.

But when her love lay cold in death,
　Sunk in the black and silent tomb,
All sere and withered was the wreath
　That wont so bright to bloom.

Yet still the withered wreath she wore ;
　She wore it at her dying hour ;
When, lo ! the wondrous garland bore
　Both leaf, and fruit, and flower !

THE KING ON THE TOWER.

FROM UHLAND.

"Da liegen sie alle, die grauen Höhen."

THE cold grey hills they bind me around,
    The darksome valleys lie sleeping below,
But the winds, as they pass o'er all this ground,
    Bring me never a sound of woe.

Oh ! for all I have suffered and striven,
   Care has embittered my cup and my feast ;
But here is the night and the dark blue heaven,
   And my soul shall be at rest.

O golden legends writ in the skies !
   I turn towards you with longing soul,
And list to the awful harmonies
   Of the Spheres as on they roll.

My hair is grey and my sight nigh gone ;
   My sword it rusteth upon the wall ;
Right have I spoken, and right have I done ;
   When shall I rest me once for all ?

O blessed rest ! O royal night !
   Wherefore seemeth the time so long
Till I see yon stars in their fullest light,
   And list to their loudest song ?

TO A VERY OLD WOMAN.

LA MOTTE FOUQUÉ.

"Und Du gingst einst, die Myrt' im Haare."

AND thou wert once a maiden fair,
    A blushing virgin warm and young :
With myrtles wreathed in golden hair,
And glossy brow that knew no care—
    Upon a bridegroom's arm you hung.

The golden locks are silvered now,
     The blushing cheek is pale and wan ;
The spring may bloom, the autumn glow,
All's one—in chimney corner thou
     Sitt'st shivering on.—

A moment—and thou sink'st to rest !
To wake perhaps an angel blest
     In the bright presence of thy Lord.
Oh, weary is life's path to all !
Hard is the strife, and light the fall,
     But wondrous the reward !

A CREDO.

I.

FOR the sole edification
Of this decent congregation,
Goodly people, by your grant
I will sing a holy chant—
    I will sing a holy chant.
If the ditty sound but oddly,
'Twas a father, wise and godly,
    Sang it so long ago—
Then sing as Martin Luther sang,
As Doctor Martin Luther sang :
"Who loves not wine, woman, and song,
He is a fool his whole life long !"

II.

He, by custom patriarchal,
Loved to see the beaker sparkle ;
And he thought the wine improved,
Tasted by the lips he loved—
    By the kindly lips he loved.
Friends, I wish this custom pious
Duly were observed by us,
    To combine love, song, wine,
And sing as Martin Luther sang,
As Doctor Martin Luther sang :
"Who loves not wine, woman, and song,
He is a fool his whole life long !"

III.

Who refuses this our Credo,
And who will not sing as we do,
Were he holy as John Knox,
I'd pronounce him heterodox !
    I'd pronounce him heterodox,

And from out this congregation,
With a solemn commination,
    Banish quick the heretic,
Who will not sing as Luther sang,
As Doctor Martin Luther sang :
" Who loves not wine, woman, and song,
He is a fool his whole life long ! "

FOUR IMITATIONS OF
BERANGER

FOUR
IMITATIONS OF BERANGER.

LE ROI D'YVETOT.

IL était un roi d'Yvetot,
   Peu connu dans l'histoire ;
Se levant tard, se couchant tôt,
   Dormant fort bien sans gloire,
Et couronné par Jeanneton
D'un simple bonnet de coton,
     Dit-on.
      Oh ! oh ! oh ! oh ! ah ! ah ! ah ! ah !
      Quel bon petit roi c'était là !
       La, la.

Il fesait ses quatre repas
 Dans son palais de chaume,
Et sur un âne, pas à pas,
 Parcourait son royaume.
Joyeux, simple et croyant le bien,
Pour toute garde il n'avait rien
  Qu'un chien.
  Oh! oh! oh! oh! ah! ah! ah! ah! &c.

Il n'avait de goût onéreux
 Qu'une soif un peu vive;
Mais, en rendant son peuple heureux,
 Il faut bien qu'un roi vive.
Lui-même à table, et sans suppôt,
Sur chaque muid levait un pot
  D'impôt.
  Oh! oh! oh! oh! ah! ah! ah! ah! &c.

Aux filles de bonnes maisons
 Comme il avait su plaire,
Ses sujets avaient cent raisons
 De le nommer leur père
D'ailleurs il ne levait de ban
Que pour tirer quatre fois l'an
 . Au blanc.
  Oh! oh! oh! oh! ah! ah! ah! ah! &c.

Il n'agrandit point ses états,
 Fut un voisin commode,
Et, modèle des potentats,
 Prit le plaisir pour code.
Ce n'est que lorsqu'il expira,
Que le peuple qui l'enterra
  Pleura.
  Oh! oh! oh! oh! ah! ah! ah! ah! &c.

On conserve encor le portrait
 De ce digne et bon prince;

C'est l'enseigne d'un cabaret
  Fameux dans la province.
Les jours de fête, bien souvent,
La foule s'écrie en buvant
    Devant :
  Oh! oh! oh! oh! ah! ah! ah! ah! &c.

THE KING OF YVETOT.

THERE was a king of Yvetot,
  Of whom renown hath little said,
Who let all thoughts of glory go,
  And dawdled half his days a-bed ;
And every night, as night came round,
By Jenny with a nightcap crowned,
          Slept very sound :
      Sing ho, ho, ho ! and he, he, he !
      That's the kind of king for me.

And every day it came to pass,
  That four lusty meals made he ;
And, step by step, upon an ass,
  Rode abroad, his realms to see ;
And wherever he did stir,
What think you was his escort, sir ?
          Why, an old cur.
      Sing ho, ho, ho ! &c.

If e'er he went into excess,
    'Twas from a somewhat lively thirst ;
But he who would his subjects bless,
    Odd's fish !—must wet his whistle first ;
And so from every cask they got,
Our king did to himself allot
                At least a pot.
        Sing ho, ho ! &c.

To all the ladies of the land,
    A courteous king, and kind, was he—
The reason why, you'll understand,
    They named him Pater Patriæ.
Each year he called his fighting men,
And marched a league from home, and then
                Marched back again.
        Sing ho, ho ! &c.

Neither by force nor false pretence,
    He sought to make his kingdom great,
And made (O princes, learn from hence)—
    " Live and let live," his rule of state.
'Twas only when he came to die,
That his people who stood by,
                Were known to cry.
        Sing ho, ho ! &c.

The portrait of this best of kings
    Is extant still, upon a sign
That on a village tavern swings,
    Famed in the country for good wine.
The people in their Sunday trim,
Filling their glasses to the brim,
                Look up to him,
        Singing ha, ha, ha ! and he, he, he !
        That's the sort of king for me.

THE KING OF BRENTFORD.

ANOTHER VERSION.

SWAIN SC.

THERE was a king in Brentford,—of whom no legends tell,
But who, without his glory,—could eat and sleep right well.
His Polly's cotton nightcap,—it was his crown of state,
He slept of evenings early,—and rose of mornings late.

All in a fine mud palace,—each day he took four meals,
And for a guard of honour—a dog ran at his heels,
Sometimes, to view his kingdoms,—rode forth this monarch good,
And then a prancing jackass—he royally bestrode.

There were no costly habits—with which this king was curst,
Except (and where's the harm on't?)—a somewhat lively thirst;
But people must pay taxes,—and kings must have their sport,
So out of every gallon—His Grace he took a quart.

He pleased the ladies round him,—with manners soft and bland ;
With reason good, they named him—the father of his land.
Each year his mighty armies—marched forth in gallant show ;
Their enemies were targets,—their bullets they were tow.

He vexed no quiet neighbour,—no useless conquest made,
But by the laws of pleasure—his peaceful realm he swayed.
And in the years he reigned,—through all this country wide,
There was no cause for weeping,—save when the good man died.

The faithful men of Brentford—do still their king deplore,
His portrait yet is swinging—beside an alehouse door.
And topers, tender-hearted,—regard his honest phiz,
And envy times departed,—that knew a reign like his.

LE GRENIER.

Je viens revoir l'asile où ma jeunesse
De la misère a subi les leçons.
J'avais vingt ans, une folle maîtresse,
De francs amis et l'amour des chansons.
Bravant le monde et les sots et les sages,
Sans avenir, riche de mon printemps,
Leste et joyeux je montais six étages.
Dans un grenier qu'on est bien à vingt ans !

C'est un grenier, point ne veux qu'on l'ignore.
Là fut mon lit, bien chétif et bien dur ;
Là fut ma table ; et je retrouve encore
Trois pieds d'un vers charbonnés sur le mur.
Apparaissez, plaisirs de mon bel âge,
Que d'un coup d'aile a fustigés le temps :
Vingt fois pour vous j'ai mis ma montre en gage.
Dans un grenier qu'on est bien à vingt ans !

Lisette ici doit surtout apparaître,
Vive, jolie, avec un frais chapeau ;
Déjà sa main à l'étroite fenêtre
Suspend son schal, en guise de rideau.
Sa robe aussi va parer ma couchette ;
Respecte, Amour, ses plis longs et flottans.
J'ai su depuis qui payait sa toilette.
Dans un grenier qu'on est bien à vingt ans !

A table un jour, jour de grande richesse,
De mes amis les voix brillaient en chœur,
Quand jusqu'ici monte un cri d'allégresse :
A Marengo Bonaparte est vainqueur.
Le canon gronde ; un autre chant commence ;
Nous célébrons tant de faits éclatans.
Les rois jamais n'envahiront la France.
Dans un grenier qu'on est bien à vingt ans !

Quittons ce toit où ma raison s'énivre.
Oh ! quil's sont loin ces jours si regrettés !
J'échangerais ce qu'il me reste à vivre
Contre un des mois qu'ici Dieu m'a comptés,
Pour rêver gloire, amour, plaisir, folie,
Pour dépenser sa vie en peu d'instans,
D'un long espoir pour la voir embellie.
Dans un grenier qu'on est bien à vingt ans !

THE GARRET.

WITH pensive eyes the little room I view,
   Where, in my youth, I weathered it so long,
With a wild mistress, a stanch friend or two,
   And a light heart still breaking into song :
Making a mock of life, and all its cares,
   Rich in the glory of my rising sun,
Lightly I vaulted up four pair of stairs,
   In the brave days when I was twenty-one.

Yes ; 'tis a garret—let him know't who will—
   There was my bed—full hard it was and small ;
My table there—and I decipher still
   Half a lame couplet charcoaled on the wall.
Ye joys, that Time hath swept with him away,
   Come to mine eyes, ye dreams of love and fun ;
For you I pawned my watch how many a day,
   In the brave days when I was twenty-one.

And see my little Jessy, first of all ;
   She comes with pouting lips and sparkling eyes :
Behold, how roguishly she pins her shawl
   Across the narrow casement, curtain-wise ;
Now by the bed her petticoat glides down,
   And when did woman look the worse in none ?
I have heard since who paid for many a gown,
   In the brave days when I was twenty-one.

One jolly evening, when my friends and I
   Made happy music with our songs and cheers,
A shout of triumph mounted up thus high,
   And distant cannon opened on our ears :
We rise,—we join in the triumphant strain,—
   Napoleon conquers—Austerlitz is won—
Tyrants shall never tread us down again,
   In the brave days when I was twenty-one.

Let us begone—the place is sad and strange—
   How far, far off, these happy times appear ;
All that I have to live I'd gladly change
   For one such month as I have wasted here—
To draw long dreams of beauty, love, and power,
   From founts of hope that never will outrun,
And drink all life's quintessence in an hour,
   Give me the days when I was twenty-one.

ROGER-BONTEMPS.

Aux gens atrabilaires
Pour exemple donné,
En un temps de misères
Roger-Bontemps est né.
Vivre obscur à sa guise,
Narguer les mécontens ;
Eh gai ! c'est la devise
Du gros Roger-Bontemps.

Du chapeau de son père
Coiffé dans les grands jours,
De roses ou de lierre
Le rajeunir toujours ;

Mettre un manteau de bure,
Vieil ami de vingt ans ;
Eh gai ! c'est la parure
Du gros Roger-Bontemps.

Posséder dans sa hutte.
Une table, un vieux lit,
Des cartes, une flûte,
Un broc que Dieu remplit ;
Un portrait de maîtresse,
Un coffre et rien dedans ;
Eh gai ! c'est la richesse
Du gros Roger-Bontemps.

Aux enfans de la ville
Montrer de petits jeux ;
Etre fesseur habile
De contes graveleux ;
Ne parler que de danse
Et d'almanachs chantans :
Eh gai ! c'est la science
Du gros Roger-Bontemps.

Faute de vins d'élite,
Sabler ceux du canton :
Préférer Marguerite
Aux dames du grand ton :
De joie et de tendresse
Remplir tous ses instans :
Eh gai ! c'est la sagesse
Du gros Roger-Bontemps.

Dire au ciel : Je me fie,
Mon père, à ta bonté ;
De ma philosophie
Pardonne le gaîté :
Que ma saison dernière
Soit encore un printemps ;
Eh gai ! c'est la prière
Du gros Roger-Bontemps.

Vous pauvres pleins d'envie,
Vous riches désireux,
Vous, dont le char dévie
Après un cours heureux ;
Vous, qui perdrez peut-être
Des titres éclatans,
Eh gai ! prenez pour maître
Le gros Roger-Bontemps.

JOLLY JACK.

WHEN fierce political debate
    Throughout the isle was storming,
And Rads attacked the throne and state,
    And Tories the reforming,
To calm the furious rage of each,
    And right the land demented,
Heaven sent us Jolly Jack, to teach
    The way to be contented.

Jack's bed was straw, 'twas warm and soft,
    His chair, a three-legged stool ;
His broken jug was emptied oft,
    Yet, somehow, always full.

His mistress' portrait decked the wall,
　　His mirror had a crack ;
Yet, gay and glad, though this was all
　　His wealth, lived Jolly Jack.

To give advice to avarice,
　　Teach pride its mean condition,
And preach good sense to dull pretence,
　　Was honest Jack's high mission.
Our simple statesman found his rule
　　Of moral in the flagon,
And held his philosophic school
　　Beneath the " George and Dragon."

When village Solons cursed the Lords,
　　And called the malt-tax sinful,
Jack heeded not their angry words,
　　But smiled and drank his skinful.
And when men wasted health and life
　　In search of rank and riches,
Jack marked aloof the paltry strife,
　　And wore his threadbare breeches.

" I enter not the church," he said,
　　" But I'll not seek to rob it ; "
So worthy Jack Joe Miller read,
　　While others studied Cobbett.
His talk it was of feast and fun ;
　　His guide the Almanack ;
From youth to age thus gaily run
　　The life of Jolly Jack.

And when Jack prayed, as oft he would
　　He humbly thanked his Maker ;
" I am," said he, " O Father good !
　　Nor Catholic nor Quaker:
Give each his creed, let each proclaim
　　His catalogue of curses ;
I trust in Thee, and not in them,
　　In Thee and in Thy mercies !

" Forgive me if, midst all Thy works,
   No hint I see of damning ;
And think there's faith among the Turks,
   And hope for e'en the Brahmin.
Harmless my mind is, and my mirth,
   And kindly is my laughter ;
I cannot see the smiling earth,
   And think there's hell hereafter."

Jack died ; he left no legacy,
   Save that his story teaches :—
Content to peevish poverty ;
   Humility to riches.
Yè scornful great, ye envious small,
   Come follow in his track ;
We all were happier, if we all
   Would copy JOLLY JACK.

IMITATION OF HORACE

IMITATION OF HORACE.

TO HIS SERVING BOY.

Persicos odi,
Puer, apparatus ;
Displicent nexæ
Philyrâ coronæ :
Mitte sectari,
Rosa quo locorum
Sera moretur.

Simplici myrto
Nihil allabores
Sedulus, curo :
Neque te ministrum
Dedecet myrtus,
Neque me sub arctâ
Vite bibentem.

AD MINISTRAM.

DEAR Lucy, you know what my wish is,—
   I hate all your Frenchified fuss :
Your silly entrées and made dishes
   Were never intended for us.
No footman in lace and in ruffles
   Need dangle behind my arm-chair ;
And never mind seeking for truffles,
   Although they be ever so rare.

But a plain leg of mutton, my Lucy,
   I prithee get ready at three :
Have it smoking, and tender and juicy,
   And what better meat can there be ?
And when it has feasted the master,
   'Twill amply suffice for the maid ;
Meanwhile I will smoke my canaster,
   And tipple my ale in the shade.

OLD FRIENDS WITH NEW FACES

OLD FRIENDS WITH NEW FACES.

THE KNIGHTLY GUERDON.

UNTRUE to my Ulric I never could be,
I vow by the saints and the blessed Marie,
Since the desolate hour when we stood by the shore,
And your dark galley waited to carry you o'er :
My faith then I plighted, my love I confess'd,
As I gave you the BATTLE-AXE marked with your crest !

---

* "WAPPING OLD STAIRS.

" Your Molly has never been false, she declares,
Since the last time we parted at Wapping Old Stairs ;
When I said that I would continue the same,
And gave you the 'bacco-box marked with my name.
When I passed a whole fortnight between decks with you,
Did I e'er give a kiss, Tom, to one of your crew ?
To be useful and kind to my Thomas I stay'd,
For his trousers I washed, and his grog too I made.

" Though you promised last Sunday to walk in the Mall
With Susan from Deptford and likewise with Sall,
In silence I stood your unkindness to hear,
And only upbraided my Tom with a tear.
Why should Sall, or should Susan, than me be more prized ?
For the heart that is true, Tom, should ne'er be despised.
Then be constant and kind, nor your Molly forsake ;
Still your trousers I'll wash, and your grog too I'll make."

When the bold barons met in my father's old hall,
Was not Edith the flower of the banquet and ball?
In the festival hour, on the lips of your bride,
Was there ever a smile save with THEE at my side?
Alone in my turret I loved to sit best,
To blazon your BANNER and broider your crest.

The knights were assembled, the tourney was gay!
Sir Ulric rode first in the warrior-mêlée.
In the dire battle-hour, when the tourney was done,
And you gave to another the wreath you had won!
Though I never reproached thee, cold, cold was my breast,
As I thought of that BATTLE-AXE, ah! and that crest!

But away with remembrance, no more will I pine
That others usurped for a time what was mine!
There's a FESTIVAL HOUR for my Ulric and me:
Once more, as of old, shall he bend at my knee;
Once more by the side of the knight I love best
Shall I blazon his BANNER and broider his crest.

THE ALMACK'S ADIEU.

YOUR Fanny was never false-hearted,
 And this she protests and she vows,
From the *triste moment* when we parted
 On the staircase of Devonshire House !
I blushed when you asked me to marry,
 I vowed I would never forget ;
And at parting I gave my dear Harry
 A beautiful vinegarette !

We spent *en province* all December,
 And I ne'er condescended to look
At Sir Charles, or the rich county member,
 Or even at that darling old Duke.
You were busy with dogs and with horses.
 Alone in my chamber I sat,
And made you the nicest of purses,
 And the smartest black satin cravat !

At night with that vile Lady Frances
 (*Je faisois moi tapisserie*)
You danced every one of the dances,
 And never once thought of poor me !
Mon pauvre petit cœur ! what a shiver
 I felt as she danced the last set ;
And you gave, *O mon Dieu !* to revive her
 My beautiful vinegarette !

Return, love ! away with coquetting ;
 This flirting disgraces a man !
And ah ! all the while you're forgetting
 The heart of your poor little Fan !
Reviens ! break away from those Circes,
 Reviens, for a nice little chat ;
And I've made you the sweetest of purses,
 And a lovely black satin cravat !

WHEN THE GLOOM IS ON THE GLEN.

WHEN the moonlight's on the mountain
  And the gloom is on the glen,
At the cross beside the fountain
  There is one will meet thee then.
At the cross beside the fountain,
  Yes, the cross beside the fountain,
There is one will meet thee then !

I have braved, since first we met, love,
  Many a danger in my course ;
But I never can forget, love,
  That dear fountain, that old cross,

Where, her mantle shrouded o'er her—
   For the winds were chilly then—
First I met my Leonora,
   When the gloom was on the glen.

Many a clime I've ranged since then, love,
   Many a land I've wandered o'er ;
But a valley like that glen, love,
   Half so dear I never sor !
Ne'er saw maiden fairer, coyer,
   Than wert thou, my true love, when
In the gloaming first I saw yer,
   In the gloaming of the glen !

THE RED FLAG.

WHERE the quivering lightning flings
　His arrows from out the clouds,
And the howling tempest sings
　And whistles among the shrouds,
'Tis pleasant, 'tis pleasant to ride
　Along the foaming brine—
Wilt be the Rover's bride?
　Wilt follow him, lady mine?
　　　　Hurrah!
For the bonny, bonny brine.

Amidst the storm and rack,
   You shall see our galley pass,
As a serpent, lithe and black,
   Glides through the waving grass.
As the vulture, swift and dark,
   Down on the ring-dove flies,
You shall see the Rover's bark
   Swoop down upon his prize.
           Hurrah !
For the bonny, bonny prize.

Over her sides we dash,
   We gallop across her deck—
Ha ! there's a ghastly gash
   On the merchant-captain's neck—
Well shot, well shot, old Ned !
   Well struck, well struck, black James !
Our arms are red, and our foes are dead,
   And we leave a ship in flames !
           Hurrah !
For the bonny, bonny flames !

DEAR JACK.

DEAR Jack, this white mug that with Guinness I fill,
And drink to the health of sweet Nan of the Hill,
Was once Tommy Tosspot's, as jovial a sot
As e'er drew a spigot, or drain'd a full pot—
In drinking all round 'twas his joy to surpass,
And with all merry tipplers he swigg'd off his glass.

One morning in summer, while seated so snug,
In the porch of his garden, discussing his jug,
Stern Death, on a sudden, to Tom did appear,
And said, " Honest Thomas, come take your last bier."
We kneaded his clay in the shape of this can,
From which let us drink to the health of my Nan.

COMMANDERS OF THE FAITHFUL.

THE Pope he is a happy man,
His Palace is the Vatican,
And there he sits and drains his can :
The Pope he is a happy man.
I often say when I'm at home,
I'd like to be the Pope of Rome.

And then there's Sultan Saladin,
That Turkish Soldan full of sin ;
He has a hundred wives at least,
By which his pleasure is increased :
I've often wished, I hope no sin,
That I were Sultan Saladin.

But no, the Pope no wife may choose,
And so I would not wear his shoes ;
No wine may drink the proud Paynim,
And so I'd rather not be him :
My wife, my wine, I love, I hope,
And would be neither Turk nor Pope.

WHEN MOONLIKE ORE THE HAZURE SEAS.

WHEN moonlike ore the hazure seas
    In soft effulgence swells,
When silver jews and balmy breaze
    Bend down the Lily's bells;
When calm and deap, the rosy sleap
    Has lapt your soal in dreems,
R Hangeline ! R lady mine !
    Dost thou remember Jeames ?

I mark thee in the Marble All,
    Where England's loveliest shine—
I say the fairest of them hall
    Is Lady Hangeline.

My soul, in desolate eclipse,
　　With recollection teems—
And then I hask, with weeping lips,
　　Dost thou remember Jeames?

Away ! I may not tell thee hall
　　This soughring heart endures—
There is a lonely sperrit-call
　　That Sorrow never cures ;
There is a little, little Star,
　　That still above me beams ;
It is the Star of Hope—but ar !
　　Dost thou remember Jeames?

KING CANUTE.

King Canute was weary-hearted ; he had reigned for years a score,
Battling, struggling, pushing, fighting, killing much and robbing
　　more ;
And he thought upon his actions, walking by the wild sea-shore.

'Twixt the Chancellor and Bishop walked the King with steps sedate,
Chamberlains and grooms came after, silversticks and goldsticks great,
Chaplains, aides-de-camp, and pages,—all the officers of state.

Sliding after like his shadow, pausing when he chose to pause,
If a frown his face contracted, straight the courtiers dropped their
　　jaws ;
If to laugh the King was minded, out they burst in loud hee-haws.

But that day a something vexed him, that was clear to old and young :
Thrice his Grace had yawned at table, when his favourite gleemen
　　sung,
Once the Queen would have consoled him, but he bade her hold her
　　tongue.

" Something ails my gracious master," cried the Keeper of the Seal.
" Sure, my lord, it is the lampreys served to dinner, or the veal ? "
" Psha ! " exclaimed the angry monarch. " Keeper, 'tis not that I feel.

" 'Tis the *heart*, and not the dinner, fool, that doth my rest impair :
Can a king be great as I am, prithee, and yet know no care ?
Oh, I'm sick, and tired, and weary."—Some one cried, " The King's
　　arm-chair ! "

Then towards the lackeys turning, quick my Lord the Keeper nodded,
Straight the King's great chair was brought him by two footmen able
　　bodied ;
Languidly he sank into it : it was comfortably wadded.

"Leading on my fierce companions," cried he, "over storm and
    brine,
I have fought and I have conquered! Where was glory like to
    mine?"
Loudly all the courtiers echoed: "Where is glory like to thine?"

"What avail me all my kingdoms? Weary am I now and old;
Those fair sons I have begotten long to see me dead and cold;
Would I were, and quiet buried underneath the silent mould!

"Oh, remorse, the writhing serpent! at my bosom tears and bites;
Horrid, horrid things I look on, though I put out all the lights;
Ghosts of ghastly recollections troop about my bed at nights.

"Cities burning, convents blazing, red with sacrilegious fires;
Mothers weeping, virgins screaming vainly for their slaughtered
    sires."—
"Such a tender conscience," cries the Bishop, "every one admires.

"But for such unpleasant bygones cease, my gracious lord, to search,
They're forgotten and forgiven by our Holy Mother Church;
Never, never does she leave her benefactors in the lurch.

"Look! the land is crowned with minsters, which your Grace's bounty
    raised;
Abbeys filled with holy men, where you and Heaven are daily praised:
You, my lord, to think of dying? on my conscience I'm amazed!"

"Nay, I feel," replied King Canute, "that my end is drawing near."
"Don't say so," exclaimed the courtiers (striving each to squeeze a
    tear).
"Sure your Grace is strong and lusty, and may live this fifty year."

"Live these fifty years!" the Bishop roared, with actions made to suit.
"Are you mad, my good Lord Keeper, thus to speak of King Canute?
Men have lived a thousand years, and sure his Majesty will do't.

"Adam, Enoch, Lamech, Cainan, Mahaleel, Methusela,
Lived nine hundred years apiece, and mayn't the King as well as
    they?"
"Fervently," exclaimed the Keeper, "fervently I trust he may."

" *He* to die ? " resumed the Bishop. " He a mortal like to *us* ?
Death was not for him intended, though *communis omnibus :*
Keeper, you are irreligious for to talk and cavil thus.

" With his wondrous skill in healing ne'er a doctor can compete,
Loathsome lepers, if he touch them, start up clean upon their feet ;
Surely he could raise the dead up, did his Highness think it meet.

" Did not once the Jewish captain stay the sun upon the hill,
And, the while he slew the foemen, bid the silver moon stand still ?
So, no doubt, could gracious Canute, if it were his sacred will."

" Might I stay the sun above us, good Sir Bishop ? " Canute cried ;
" Could I bid the silver moon to pause upon her heavenly ride ?
If the moon obeys my orders, sure I can command the tide.

" Will the advancing waves obey me, Bishop, if I make the sign ? "
Said the Bishop, bowing lowly, " Land and sea, my lord, are thine.'
Canute turned towards the ocean—" Back ! " he said, " thou foaming
       brine.

" From the sacred shore I stand on, I command thee to retreat ;
Venture not, thou stormy rebel, to approach thy master's seat :
Ocean, be thou still ! I bid thee come not nearer to my feet !"

But the sullen ocean answered with a louder, deeper roar,
And the rapid waves drew nearer, falling sounding on the shore ;
Back the Keeper and the Bishop, back the King and courtiers bore.

And he sternly bade them never more to kneel to human clay,
But alone to praise and worship That which earth and seas obey :
And his golden crown of empire never wore he from that day.
King Canute is dead and gone : Parasites exist alway.

FRIAR'S SONG.

SOME love the matin-chimes, which tell
 The hour of prayer to sinner :
But better far's the mid-day bell,
 Which speaks the hour of dinner ;

For when I see a smoking fish,
 Or capon drown'd in gravy,
Or noble haunch on silver dish,
 Full glad I sing my ave.

My pulpit is an alehouse bench,
 Whereon I sit so jolly ;
A smiling rosy country wench
 My saint and patron holy.
I kiss her cheek so red and sleek,
 I press her ringlets wavy,
And in her willing ear I speak
 A most religious ave.

And if I'm blind, yet Heaven is kind,
 And holy saints forgiving ;
For sure he leads a right good life
 Who thus admires good living.
Above, they say, our flesh is air,
 Our blood celestial ichor :
Oh, grant ! mid all the changes there,
 They may not change our liquor !

ATRA CURA.

BEFORE I lost my five poor wits,
I mind me of a Romish clerk,
Who sang how Care, the phantom dark,
Beside the belted horseman sits.
Methought I saw the grisly sprite
Jump up but now behind my Knight.

And though he gallop as he may,
I mark that cursed monster black
Still sits behind his honour's back,
Tight squeezing of his heart alway.

Like two black Templars sit they there,
Beside one crupper, Knight and Care.

No knight am I with pennoned spear,
To prance upon a bold destrere :
I will not have black Care prevail
Upon my long-eared charger's tail ;
For lo, I am a witless fool,
And laugh at Grief and ride a mule.

REQUIESCAT.

UNDER the stone you behold,
Buried, and coffined, and cold,
Lieth Sir Wilfrid the Bold.

Always he marched in advance,
Warring in Flanders and France,
Doughty with sword and with lance.

Famous in Saracen fight,
Rode in his youth the good knight,
Scattering Paynims in flight.

Brian, the Templar untrue,
Fairly in tourney he slew,
Saw Hierusalem too.

Now he is buried and gone,
Lying beneath the grey stone :
Where shall you find such a one ?

Long time his widow deplored,
Weeping the fate of her lord,
Sadly cut off by the sword.

When she was eased of her pain,
Came the good Lord Athelstane,
When her ladyship married again.

THE WILLOW-TREE.

KNOW ye the willow-tree
  Whose grey leaves quiver,
Whispering gloomily
  To yon pale river?

Lady, at even-tide
  Wander not near it :
They say its branches hide
  A sad, lost spirit !

Once to the willow-tree
  A maid came fearful ;
Pale seemed her cheek to be,
  Her blue eye tearful.
Soon as she saw the tree,
  Her step moved fleeter ;
No one was there—ah me !
  No one to meet her !

Quick beat her heart to hear
  The far bells' chime
Toll from the chapel-tower
  The trysting time :
But the red sun went down
  In golden flame,
And though she looked round,
  Yet no one came !

Presently came the night,
  Sadly to greet her,—
Moon in her silver light,
  Stars in their glitter ;
Then sank the moon away
  Under the billow,
Still wept the maid alone—
  There by the willow !

Through the long darkness,
  By the stream rolling,
Hour after hour went on
  Tolling and tolling.
Long was the darkness,
  Lonely and stilly ;
Shrill came the night-wind,
  Piercing and chilly.

Shrill blew the morning breeze,
  Biting and cold,
Bleak peers the grey dawn
  Over the wold.
Bleak over moor and stream
  Looks the grey dawn,
Grey, with dishevelled hair,
Still stands the willow there—
  THE MAID IS GONE!

Domine, Domine!
  Sing we a litany,—
Sing for poor maiden-hearts broken and weary;
  Domine, Domine!
Sing we a litany,
  Wail we and weep we a wild Miserere!

THE WILLOW-TREE.

(ANOTHER VERSION.)

I.

LONG by the willow-trees
  Vainly they sought her,
Wild rang the mother's screams
  O'er the grey water:
"Where is my lovely one?
  Where is my daughter?

II.

"Rouse thee, sir constable—
  Rouse thee and look;
Fisherman, bring your net,
  Boatman your hook.
Beat in the lily-beds,
  Dive in the brook!"

III.

Vainly the constable
  Shouted and called her;
Vainly the fisherman
  Beat the green alder,
Vainly he flung the net,
  Never it hauled her!

IV.

Mother beside the fire
  Sat, her nightcap in;
Father, in easy chair,
  Gloomily napping,
When at the window-sill
  Came a light tapping!

P 2

V.

And a pale countenance
   Looked through the casement.
Loud beat the mother's heart,
   Sick with amazement,
And at the vision which
   Came to surprise her,
Shrieked in an agony—
   " Lor ! it's Elizar ! "

VI.

Yes, 'twas Elizabeth —
   Yes, 'twas their girl ;
Pale was her cheek, and her
   Hair out of curl.
" Mother ! " the loving one,
   Blushing, exclaimed
" Let not your innocent
   Lizzy be blamed.

VII.

" Yesterday, going to aunt
   Jones's to tea,
Mother, dear mother, I
   Forgot the door-key !
And as the night was cold,
   And the way steep,
Mrs. Jones kept me to
   Breakfast and sleep."

VIII.

Whether her Pa and Ma
   Fully believed her,
That we shall never know,
   Stern they received her ;
And for the work of that
   Cruel, though short, night,
Sent her to bed without
   Tea for a fortnight.

IX.

MORAL.

Hey diddle diddlety,
Cat and the Fiddlety,
Maidens of England, take caution by she!
Let love and suicide
Never tempt you aside,
And always remember to take the door-key.

LYRA HIBERNICA.

THE POEMS OF THE MOLONY OF KILBALLYMOLONY.

LYRA HIBERNICA.

THE POEMS OF THE MOLONY OF KILBALLYMOLONY.

THE PIMLICO PAVILION.

Ye pathrons of janius, Minerva and Vanius,
  Who sit on Parnassus, that mountain of snow,
Descind from your station and make observation
  Of the Prince's pavilion in sweet Pimlico.

This garden, by jakurs, is forty poor acres,
  (The garner he tould me, and sure ought to know ;)
And yet greatly bigger, in size and in figure,
  Than the Phanix itself, seems the Park Pimlico.

O 'tis there that the spoort is, when the Queen and the Court is
  Walking magnanimous all of a row,
Forgetful what state is among the pataties
  And the pine-apple gardens of sweet Pimlico.

There in blossoms odorous the birds sing a chorus
  Of " God save the Queen " as they hop to and fro ;
And you sit on the binches and hark to the finches,
  Singing melodious in sweet Pimlico.

There shuiting their phanthasies, they pluck polyanthuses
  That round in the gardens resplindently grow,
Wid roses and jessimins, and other sweet specimins,
  Would charm bould Linnayus in sweet Pimlico.

You see when you inther, and stand in the cinther,
   Where the roses, and necturns, and collyflowers blow,
A hill so tremindous, it tops the top-windows
   Of the elegant houses of famed Pimlico.

And when you've ascinded that precipice splindid
   You see on its summit a wondtherful show—
A lovely Swish building, all painting and gilding,
   The famous Pavilion of sweet Pimlico.

Prince Albert, of Flandthers, that Prince of Commandthers,
   (On whom my best blessings hereby I bestow,)
With goold and vermilion has decked that Pavilion,
   Where the Queen may take tay in her sweet Pimlico.

There's lines from John Milton the chamber all gilt on,
   And pictures beneath them that's shaped like a bow;
I was greatly astounded to think that that Roundhead
   Should find an admission to famed Pimlico.

O lovely's each fresco, and most picturesque O ;
   And while round the chamber astonished I go,
I think Dan Maclise's it baits all the pieces
   Surrounding the cottage of famed Pimlico.

Eastlake has the chimney, (a good one to limn he,)
   And a vargin he paints with a sarpent below|;
While bulls, pigs, and panthers, and other enchanthers,
   Are painted by Landseer in sweet Pimlico.

And nature smiles opposite, Stanfield he copies it ;
   O'er Claude or Poussang sure 'tis he that may crow :
But Sir Ross's best faiture is small miniáture—
   He shouldn't paint frescoes in famed Pimlico.

There's Leslie and Uwins has rather small doings ;
   There's Dyce, as brave masther as England can show ;
And the flowers and the sthrawberries, sure he no dauber is,
   That painted the panels of famed Pimlico.

In the pictures from Walther Scott, never a fault there's got,
   Sure the marble's as natural as thrue Scaglio ;

And the Chamber Pompayen is sweet to take tay in,
  And ait butther'd muffins in sweet Pimlico.

There's landscapes by Gruner, both solar and lunar,
  Them two little Doyles, too, deserve a bravo;
Wid de piece by young Townsend, (for janius abounds in't;)
  And that's why he's shuited to paint Pimlico.

That picture of Severn's is worthy of rever'nce,
  But some I won't mintion is rather so so;
For sweet philosóphy, or crumpets and coffee,
  O where's a Pavilion like sweet Pimlico?

O to praise this Pavilion would puzzle Quintilian,
  Daymosthenes, Brougham, or young Cicero;
So, heavenly Goddess, d'ye pardon my modesty,
  And silence, my lyre! about sweet Pimlico.

THE CRYSTAL PALACE.

WITH ganial foire
Thransfuse me loyre,
Ye sacred nympths of Pindus,
The whoile I sing
That wondthrous thing,
The Palace made o' windows !

Say, Paxton, truth,
Thou wondthrous youth,
What sthroke of art celistial,
What power was lint
You to invint
This combineetion cristial.

O would before
That Thomas Moore,
Likewoise the late Lord Boyron,
Thim aigles sthrong
Of godlike song,
Cast oi on that cast oiron !

And saw thim walls,
And glittering halls,
Thim rising slendther columns,
Which I, poor pote,
Could not denote,
No, not in twinty vollums.

My Muse's words
Is like the bird's
That roosts beneath the panes there ;
Her wings she spoils
'Gainst them bright toiles,
And cracks her silly brains there.

This Palace tall,
This Cristial Hall,
Which Imperors might covet,
Stands in High Park
Like Noah's Ark,
A rainbow bint above it.

The towers and fanes,
In other scaynes,
The fame of this will undo,
Saint Paul's big doom,
Saint Payther's Room,
And Dublin's proud Rotundo.

'Tis here that roams,
As well becomes
Her dignitee and stations,
Victoria Great,
And houlds in state
The Congress of the Nations.

Her subjects pours
From distant shores,
Her Injians and Canajians;
And also we,
Her kingdoms three,
Attind with our allagiance.

Here come likewise
Her bould allies,
Both Asian and Europian;
From East and West
They send their best
To fill her Coornucopean.

I seen (thank Grace!)
This wondthrous place
(His Noble Honour Misther
H. Cole it was
That gave the pass,
And let me see what is there).

With conscious proide
I stud insoide
And look'd the World's Great Fair in,
Until me sight
Was dazzled quite,
And couldn't see for staring.

There's holy saints
And window paints,
By Maydiayval Pugin ;
Alhamborough Jones
Did paint the tones
Of yellow and gambouge in.

There's fountains there
And crosses fair ;
There's water-gods with urrns :
There's organs three,
To play, d'ye see ?
" God save the Queen," by turrns.

There's statues bright
Of marble white,
Of silver, and of copper ;
And some in zinc,
And some, I think,
That isn't over proper.

There's staym ingynes,
That stands in lines,
Enormous and amazing,
That squeal and snort
Like whales in sport,
Or elephants a-grazing.

There's carts and gigs,
And pins for pigs,
There's dibblers and there's harrows,
And ploughs like toys
For little boys,
And ilegant wheel-barrows.

For thim genteels
Who ride on wheels,
There's plenty to indulge 'em :
There's droskys snug
From Paytersbug,
And vayhycles from Bulgium.

There's cabs on stands
And shandthry danns ;
There's waggons from New York here ;
There's Lapland sleighs
Have cross'd the seas,
And jaunting cyars from Cork here.

Amazed I pass
From glass to glass,
Deloighted I survey 'em ;
Fresh wondthers grows
Before me nose
In this sublime Musayum !

Look, here's a fan
From far Japan,
A sabre from Damasco :
There's shawls ye get
From far Thibet,
And cotton prints from Glasgow.

There's German flutes,
Marocky boots,
And Naples macaronies ;
Bohaymia
Has sent Bohay ;
Polonia her polonies.

There's granite flints
That's quite imminse,
There's sacks of coals and fuels,
There's swords and guns,
And soap in tuns,
And ginger-bread and jewels.

There's taypots there,
  And cannons rare ;
There's coffins fill'd with roses ;
  There's canvas tints,
  Teeth insthrumints,
And shuits of clothes by MOSES.

There's lashins more
  Of things in store,
But thim I don't remimber ;
  Nor could disclose
  Did I compose
From May time to Novimber !

Ah, JUDY thru !
  With eyes so blue,
That you were here to view it !
  And could I screw
  But tu pound tu,
'Tis I would thrait you to it !

So let us raise
  Victoria's praise,
And Albert's proud condition,
  That takes his ayse
  As he surveys
This Cristial Exhibition.

1851.

MOLONY'S LAMENT.

O TIM, did you hear of thim Saxons,
  And read what the peepers report?
They're goan to recal the Liftinant,
  And shut up the Castle and Coort!
Our desolate counthry of Oireland
  They're bint, the blagyards, to desthroy,
And now having murdthered our counthry,
  They're goin to kill the Viceroy,
      Dear boy;
  'Twas he was our proide and our joy!

And will we no longer behould him,
  Surrounding his carriage in throngs,
As he waves his cocked-hat from the windies,
  And smiles to his bould aid-de-congs?
I liked for to see the young haroes,
  All shoining with sthripes and with stars,
A horsing about in the Phaynix,
  And winking the girls in the cyars,
      Like Mars,
  A smokin' their poipes and cigyars.

Dear Mitchell exoiled to Bermudies,
  Your beautiful oilids you'll ope,
And there'll be an abondance of croyin'
  From O'Brine at the Keep of Good Hope,
When they read of this news in the peepers,
  Acrass the Atlantical wave,
That the last of the Oirish Liftinints
  Of the oisland of Seents has tuck lave.
      God save
  The Queen—she should betther behave.

And what's to become of poor Dame Sthreet,
　　And who'll ait the puffs and the tarts,
Whin the Coort of imparial splindor
　　From Doblin's sad city departs?
And who'll have the fiddlers and pipers,
　　When the deuce of a Coort there remains?
And where'll be the bucks and the ladies,
　　To hire the Coort-shuits and the thrains?
　　　　In sthrains,
It's thus that ould Erin complains!

There's Counsellor Flanagan's leedy,
　　'Twas she in the Coort didn't fail,
And she wanted a plinty of popplin,
　　For her dthress, and her flounce, and her tail;
She bought it of Misthress O'Grady,
　　Eight shillings a yard tabinet,
But now that the Coort is concluded,
　　The divvle a yard will she get;
　　　　I bet,
Bedad, that she wears the old set.

There's Surgeon O'Toole and Miss Leary,
　　They'd daylings at Madam O'Riggs';
Each year at the dthrawing-room sayson,
　　They mounted the neatest of wigs.
When Spring, with its buds and its dasies,
　　Comes out in her beauty and bloom,
Thim tu'll never think of new jasies,
　　Becase there is no dthrawing-room,
　　　　For whom
They'd choose the expense to ashume.

There's Alderman Toad and his lady,
　　'Twas they gave the Clart and the Poort,
And the poine-apples, turbots, and lobsters,
　　To feast the Lord Liftinint's Coort.
But now that the quality's goin,
　　I warnt that the aiting will stop,
And you'll get at the Alderman's teeble
　　The devil a bite or a dthrop,
　　　　Or chop;
And the butcher may shut up his shop.

Yes, the grooms and the ushers are goin,
   And his Lordship, the dear honest man,
And the Duchess, his eemiable leedy,
   And Corry, the bould Connellan,
And little Lord Hyde and the childthren,
   And the Chewter and Governess tu ;
And the servants are packing their boxes,—
   Oh, murther, but what shall I due
             Without you ?
  O Meery, with ois of the blue !

MR. MOLONY'S ACCOUNT OF THE BALL

GIVEN TO THE NEPAULESE AMBASSADOR BY THE PENINSULAR AND ORIENTAL COMPANY.

O WILL ye choose to hear the news,
  Bedad I cannot pass it o'er :
I'll tell you all about the Ball
  To the Naypaulase Ambassador.
Begor ! this fête all balls does bate
  At which I've worn a pump, and I
Must here relate the splendthor great
  Of th' Oriental Company.

These men of sinse dispoised expinse,
  To fête these black Achilleses.
"We'll show the blacks," says they, "Almack's,
  "And take the rooms at Willis's."
With flags and shawls, for these Nepauls,
  They hung the rooms of Willis up,
And decked the walls, and stairs, and halls,
  With roses and with lilies up.

And Jullien's band it tuck its stand
  So sweetly in the middle there,
And soft bassoons played heavenly chunes,
  And violins did fiddle there.
And when the Coort was tired of spoort,
  I'd lave you, boys, to think there was
A nate buffet before them set,
  Where lashins of good dhrink there was.

At ten before the ball-room door,
  His moighty Excelléncy was,
He smoiled and bowed to all the crowd,
  So gorgeous and immense he was.

His dusky shuit, sublime and mute,
  Into the door-way followed him ;
And O the noise of the blackguard boys,
  As they hurrood and hollowed him !

The noble Chair* stud at the stair,
  And bade the dthrums to thump ; and he
Did thus evince, to that Black Prince,
  The welcome of his Company.
O fair the girls, and rich the curls,
  And bright the oys you saw there, was ;
And fixed each oye, ye there could spoi,
  On Gineral Jung Bahawther, was !

This Gineral great then tuck his sate,
  With all the other ginerals,
(Bedad his troat, his belt, his coat,
  All bleezed with precious minerals ;)
And as he there, with princely air,
  Recloinin on his cushion was,
All round about his royal chair
  The squeezin and the pushin was.

O Pat, such girls, such Jukes, and Earls,
  Such fashion and nobilitee !
Just think of Tim, and fancy him
  Amidst the hoigh gentilitee !
There was Lord De L'Huys, and the Portygeese
  Ministher and his lady there,
And I reckonised, with much surprise,
  Our messmate, Bob O'Grady, there ;

There was Baroness Brunow, that looked like Juno,
  And Baroness Rehausen there,
And Countess Roullier, that looked peculiar
  Well, in her robes of gauze in there.

---

* James Matheson, Esq., to whom, and the Board of Directors of the
Peninsular and Oriental Company, I, Timotheus Molony, late stoker on
board the " Iberia," the " Lady Mary Wood," the " Tagus," and the Oriental
Steamships, humbly dedicate this production of my grateful muse.

There was Lord Crowhurst (I knew him first,
	When only Mr. Pips he was),
And Mick O'Toole, the great big fool,
	That after supper tipsy was.

There was Lord Fingall, and his ladies all,
	And Lords Killeen and Dufferin,
And Paddy Fife, with his fat wife;
	I wondther how he could stuff her in.
There was Lord Belfast, that by me past,
	And seemed to ask how should *I* go there?
And the Widow Macrae, and Lord A. Hay,
	And the Marchioness of Sligo there.

Yes, Jukes, and Earls, and diamonds, and pearls,
	And pretty girls, was spooring there;
And some beside (the rogues!) I spied,
	Behind the windiés, coorting there.
O, there's one I know, bedad, would show
	As beautiful as any there,
And I'd like to hear the pipers blow,
	And shake a fut with Fanny there!

THE BATTLE OF LIMERICK.

YE Genii of the nation,
  Who look with veneration,
And Ireland's desolation onsaysingly deplore ;
  Ye sons of General Jackson,
  Who thrample on the Saxon,
Attend to the thransaction upon Shannon shore.

When William, Duke of Schumbug,
A tyrant and a humbug,
With cannon and with thunder on our city bore,
Our fortitude and valliance
Insthructed his battalions
To rispict the galliant Irish upon Shannon shore.

Since that capitulation,
No city in this nation
So grand a reputation could boast before,
As Limerick prodigious,
That stands with quays and bridges,
And the ships up to the windies of the Shannon shore.

A chief of ancient line,
'Tis William Smith O'Brine
Reprisints this darling Limerick, this ten years or more :
O the Saxons can't endure
To see him on the flure,
And thrimble at the Cicero from Shannon shore !

This valliant son of Mars
Had been to visit Par's,
That land of Revolution, that grows the tricolor ;
And to welcome his returrn
From pilgrimages furren,
We invited him to tay on the Shannon shore.

Then we summoned to our board
Young Meagher of the sword ;
'Tis he will sheathe that battle-axe in Saxon gore :
And Mitchil of Belfast
We bade to our repast,
To dthrink a dish of coffee on the Shannon shore.

Convaniently to hould
These patriots so bould,
We tuck the opportunity of Tim Doolan's store ;
And with ornamints and banners
(As becomes gintale good manners)
We made the loveliest tay-room upon Shannon shore

'Twould binifit your sowls,
To see the butthered rowls,
The sugar-tongs and sangwidges and craim galyore,
And the muffins and the crumpets,
And the band of harps and thrumpets,
To celebrate the sworry upon Shannon shore.

Sure the Imperor of Bohay
Would be proud to dthrink the tay
That Misthress Biddy Rooney for O'Brine did pour;
And, since the days of Strongbow,
There never was such Congo—
Mitchil dthrank six quarts of it—by Shannon shore.

But Clarndon and Corry
Connellan beheld this sworry
With rage and imulation in their black hearts' core;
And they hired a gang of ruffins
To interrupt the muffins
And the fragrance of the Congo on the Shannon shore.

When full of tay and cake,
O'Brine began to spake;
But juice a one could hear him, for a sudden roar
Of a ragamuffin rout
Began to yell and shout,
And frighten the propriety of Shannon shore.

As Smith O'Brine harangued,
They batthered and they banged:
Tim Doolan's doors and windies down they tore;
They smashed the lovely windies
(Hung with muslin from the Indies),
Purshuing of their shindies upon Shannon shore.

With throwing of brickbats,
Drowned puppies and dead rats,
These ruffin democrats themselves did lower;
Tin kettles, rotten eggs,
Cabbage-stalks, and wooden legs,
They flung among the patriots of Shannon shore.

O the girls began to scrame
And upset the milk and crame ;
And the honourable gintlemin, they cursed and swore :
And Mitchil of Belfast,
'Twas he that looked aghast,
When they roasted him in effigy by Shannon shore.

O the lovely tay was spilt
On that day of Ireland's guilt ;
Says Jack Mitchil, " I am kilt ! Boys, where's the back door ?
'Tis a national disgrace :
Let me go and veil me face ;"
And he boulted with quick pace from the Shannon shore.

" Cut down the bloody horde !"
Says Meagher of the sword,
" This conduct would disgrace any blackamore ;"
But the best use Tommy made
Of his famous battle blade
Was to cut his own stick from the Shannon shore.

Immortal Smith O'Brine
Was raging like a line ;
'Twould have done your sowl good to have heard him roar ;
In his glory he arose,
And he rush'd upon his foes,
But they hit him on the nose by the Shannon shore.

Then the Futt and the Dthragoons
In squadthrons and platoons,
With their music playing chunes, down upon us bore ;
And they bate the rattatoo,
But the Peelers came in view,
And ended the shaloo on the Shannon shore.

LARRY O'TOOLE.

YOU'VE all heard of Larry O'Toole,
Of the beauiful town of Drumgoole;
  He had but one eye,
  To ogle ye by—
Oh, murther, but that was a jew'l!
   A fool
He made of de girls, dis O'Toole.

'Twas he was the boy didn't fail,
That tuck down pataties and mail ;
　　　He never would shrink
　　　From any sthrong dthrink,
Was it whisky or Drogheda ale ;
　　　　I'm bail
This Larry would swallow a pail.

Oh, many a night at the bowl,
With Larry I've sot cheek by jowl ;
　　　He's gone to his rest,
　　　Where there's dthrink of the best,
And so let us give his old sowl
　　　　A howl,
For 'twas he made the noggin to rowl.

THE ROSE OF FLORA.

SENT BY A YOUNG GENTLEMAN OF QUALITY TO MISS BR-DY, OF CASTLE BRADY.

ON Brady's tower there grows a flower,
  It is the loveliest flower that blows,—
At Castle Brady there lives a lady,
  (And how I love her no one knows);
Her name is Nora, and the goddess Flora
  Presents her with this blooming rose.

"O Lady Nora," says the goddess Flora,
  "I've many a rich and bright parterre;
In Brady's towers there's seven more flowers,
  But you're the fairest lady there:
Not all the county, nor Ireland's bounty,
  Can projuice a treasure that's half so fair!"

What cheek is redder? sure roses fed her!
  Her hair is maregolds, and her eye of blew.
Beneath her eyelid, is like the vi'let,
  That darkly glistens with gentle jew!
The lily's nature is not surely whiter
  Than Nora's neck is,—and her arrums too.

"Come, gentle Nora," says the goddess Flora,
  "My dearest creature, take my advice:
There is a poet, full well you know it,
  Who spends his lifetime in heavy sighs,—
Young Redmond Barry, 'tis him you'll marry,
  If rhyme and raisin you'd choose likewise."

THE LAST IRISH GRIEVANCE.

ON reading of the general indignation occasioned in Ireland by the
appointment of a Scotch Professor to one of HER MAJESTY'S Godless
Colleges, MASTER MOLLOY MOLONY, brother of THADDEUS MOLONY,
ESQ., of the Temple, a youth only fifteen years of age, dashed off the
following spirited lines :—

As I think of the insult that's done to this nation,
  Red tears of rivinge from me faytures I wash,
And uphold in this pome, to the world's daytistation,
  The sleeves that appointed PROFESSOR M'COSH.

I look round me counthre, renowned by exparience,
  And see midst her childthren, the witty, the wise,—

Whole hayps of logicians, potes, schollars, grammarians,
    All ayger for pleeces, all panting to rise ;

I gaze round the world in its utmost diminsion ;
    LARD JAHN and his minions in Council I ask,
Was there ever a Government-pleece (with a pinsion)
    But children of Erin were fit for that task ?

What, Erin beloved, is thy fetal condition ?
    What shame in aych boosom must rankle and burrun,
To think that our countree has ne'er a logician
    In the hour of her deenger will surrev her turrun !

On the logic of Saxons there's little reliance,
    And, rather from Saxon than gather its rules,
I'd stamp under feet the base book of his science,
    And spit on his chair as he taught in the schools !

O false SIR JOHN KANE ! is it thus that you praych me ?
    I think all your Queen's Universitees Bosh ;
And if you've no neetive Professor to taych me,
    I scawurn to be learned by the Saxon M'COSH.

There's WISEMAN and CHUME, and His Grace the Lord Primate,
    That sinds round the box, and the world will subscribe ;
'Tis they'll build a College that's fit for our climate,
    And taych me the saycrets I burn to imboibe !

'Tis there as a Student of Science I'll enther,
    Fair Fountain of Knowledge, of Joy, and Contint !
SAINT PATHRICK'S sweet Statue shall stand in the centher,
    And wink his dear oi every day during Lint.

And good DOCTOR NEWMAN, that praycher unwary,
    'Tis he shall preside the Academee School,
And quit the gay robe of ST. PHILIP of Neri,
    To wield the soft rod of ST. LAWRENCE O'TOOLE !

BALLADS OF POLICEMAN X

THE

BALLADS of POLICEMAN X.

THE WOFLE NEW BALLAD OF JANE RONEY AND
MARY BROWN.

An igstrawnary tail I vill tell you this veek—
I stood in the Court of A'Beckett the Beak,
Vere Mrs. Jane Roney, a vidow, I see,
Who charged Mary Brown with a robbin of she.

This Mary was pore and in misery once,
And she came to Mrs. Roney it's more than twelve monce.
She adn't got no bed, nor no dinner nor no tea,
And kind Mrs. Roney gave Mary all three.

Mrs. Roney kep Mary for ever so many veeks,
(Her conduct disgusted the best of all Beax,)
She kep her for nothink, as kind as could be,
Never thinkin that this Mary was a traitor to she.

"Mrs. Roney, O Mrs. Roney, I feel very ill ;
Will you just step to the Doctor's for to fetch me a pill?"
"That I will, my pore Mary," Mrs. Roney says she ;
And she goes off to the Doctor's as quickly as may be.

No sooner on this message Mrs. Roney was sped,
Than hup gits vicked Mary, and jumps out a bed ;
She hopens all the trunks without never a key—
She bustes all the boxes, and vith them makes free.

R 2

Mrs. Roney's best linning, gownds, petticoats, and close,
Her children's little coats and things, her boots, and her hose,
She packed them, and she stole 'em, and avay vith them did flee
Mrs. Roney's situation—you may think vat it vould be !

Of Mary, ungrateful, who had served her this vay,
Mrs. Roney heard nothink for a long year and a day.
Till last Thursday, in Lambeth, ven whom should she see
But this Mary, as had acted so ungrateful to she ?

She was leaning on the helbo of a worthy young man,
They were going to be married, and were walkin hand in hand ;
And the Church bells was a ringing for Mary and he,
And the parson was ready, and a waitin for his fee.

When up comes Mrs. Roney, and faces Mary Brown,
Who trembles, and castes her eyes upon the ground.
She calls a jolly pleaseman, it happens to be me ;
I charge this young woman, Mr. Pleaseman, says she.

" Mrs. Roney, o, Mrs. Roney, o, do let me go,
I acted most ungrateful I own, and I know,
But the marriage bell is a ringin, and the ring you may see,
And this young man is a waitin," says Mary says she.

" I don't care three fardens for the parson and clark,
And the bell may keep ringin from noon day to dark.
Mary Brown, Mary Brown, you must come along with me ;
And I think this young man is lucky to be free."

So, in spite of the tears which bejew'd Mary's cheek,
I took that young gurl to A'Beckett the Beak ;
That exlent Justice demanded her plea—
But never a sullable said Mary said she.

On account of her conduck so base and so vile,
That wicked young gurl is committed for trile,

And if she's transpawted beyond the salt sea,
It's a proper reward for such willians as she.

Now you young gurls of Southwark for Mary who veep,
From pickin and stealin your ands you must keep,
Or it may be my dooty, as it was Thursday veek,
To pull you all hup to A'Beckett the Beak.

THE THREE CHRISTMAS WAITS.

My name is Pleaceman X ;
  Last night I was in bed,
A dream did me perplex,
  Which came into my Edd.
I dreamed I sor three Waits
  A playing of their tune,
At Pimlico Palace gates,
  All underneath the moon.
One puffed a hold French horn,
  And one a hold Banjo,
And one chap seedy and torn
  A Hirish pipe did blow.
They sadly piped and played,
  Dexcribing of their fates ;
And this was what they said,
  Those three pore Christmas Waits :—

"When this black year began,
  This Eighteen-forty-eight,
I was a great great man,
  And king both vise and great,
And Munseer Guizot by me did show
  As Minister of State.

" But Febuwerry came,
  And brought a rabble rout,
And me and my good dame
  And children did turn out,
And us, in spite of all our right,
  Sent to the right about.

" I left my native ground,
    I left my kin and kith,
I left my royal crownd,
    Vich I couldn't travel vith,
And without a pound came to English ground
    In the name of Mr. Smith.

" Like any anchorite
    I've lived since I came here,
I've kep myself quite quite,
    I've drank the small small beer,
And the vater, you see, disagrees vith me
    And all my famly dear.

" O Tweeleries so dear,
    O darling Pally Royl,
Vas it to finish here
    That I did trouble and toyl?
That all my plans should break in my ands,
    And should on me recoil?

" My state I fenced about
    Vith baynicks and vith guns ;
My gals I portioned hout,
    Rich vives I got my sons ;
O varn't it crule to lose my rule,
    My money and lands at once ?

" And so, vith arp and woice,
    Both troubled and shagreened,
I bid you to rejoice,
    O glorious England's Queend !
And never have to veep, like pore Louis-Phileep,
    Because you out are cleaned.

" O Prins, so brave and stout,
    I stand before your gate ;
Pray send a trifle hout
    To me, your pore old Vait ;
For nothink could be vuss than it's been along vith us
    In this year Forty-eight."

"Ven this bad year began,"
　　The nex man said, saysee,
" I vas a Journeyman,
　　A taylor black and free,
And my wife went out and chaired about,
　　And my name's the bold Cuffee.

" The Queen and Halbert both
　　I swore I would confound,
I took a hawfle hoath
　　To drag them to the ground ;
And sevral more with me they swore
　　Aginst the British Crownd.

" Aginst her Pleacemen all
　　We said we'd try our strenth ;
Her scarlick soldiers tall
　　We vow'd we'd lay full lenth :
And out we came, in Freedom's name,
　　Last Aypril was the tenth.

" Three 'undred thousand snobs
　　Came out to stop the vay,
Vith sticks vith iron knobs,
　　Or else we'd gained the day.
The harmy quite kept out of sight,
　　And so ve vent avay.

" Next day the Pleacemen came—
　　Rewenge it was their plann—
And from my good old dame
　　They took her tailor-mann :
And the hard hard beak did me bespeak
　　To Newgit in the Wann.

" In that etrocious Cort
　　The Jewry did agree ;
The Judge did me transport,
　　To go beyond the sea :
And so for life, from his dear wife
　　They took poor old Cuffee.

" O Halbert, Appy Prince !
   With children round your knees,
Ingraving ansum Prints,
   And taking hoff your hease ;
O think of me, the old Cuffee,
   Beyond the solt solt seas !

" Although I'm hold and black,
   My hanguish is most great ;
Great Prince, O call me back,
   And I vill be your Vait !
And never no more vill break the Lor,
   As I did in 'Forty-eight."

The tailer thus did close
   (A pore old blackymore rogue),
When a dismal gent uprose,
   And spoke with Hirish brogue :
" I'm Smith O'Brine, of Royal Line,
   Descended from Rory Ogue.

" When great O'Connle died,
   That man whom all did trust,
That man whom Henglish pride
   Beheld with such disgust,
Then Erin free fixed eyes on me,
   And swoar I should be fust.

" ' The glorious Hirish Crown,'
   Says she, ' it shall be thine :
Long time, it's wery well known,
   You kep it in your line ;
That diadem of hemerald gem
   Is yours, my Smith O'Brine.

" ' Too long the Saxon churl
   Our land encumbered hath ;
Arise, my Prince, my Earl,
   And brush them from thy path :
Rise, mighty Smith, and sveep 'em vith
   The besom of your wrath.'

" Then in my might I rose,
    My country I surveyed,
I saw it filled with foes,
    I viewed them undismayed ;
' Ha, ha !' says I, ' the harvest's high,
    I'll reap it with my blade.'

" My warriors I enrolled,
    They rallied round their lord ;
And cheafs in council old
    I summoned to the board—
Wise Doheny and Duffy bold,
    And Meagher of the Sword.

" I stood on Slievenamaun,
    They came with pikes and bills ;
They gathered in the dawn,
    Like mist upon the hills,
And rushed adown the mountain side
    Like twenty thousand rills.

" Their fortress we assail ;
    Hurroo ! my boys, hurroo !
The bloody Saxons quail
    To hear the wild shaloo :
Strike, and prevail, proud Innesfail,
    O'Brine aboo, aboo !

" Our people they defied ;
    They shot at 'em like savages,
Their bloody guns they plied
    With sanguinary ravages :
Hide, blushing Glory, hide
    That day among the cabbages !

" And so no more I'll say,
    But ask your Mussy great,
And humbly sing and pray,
    Your Majesty's poor Wait :
Your Smith O'Brine in 'Forty-nine
    Will blush for 'Forty-eight."

LINES ON A LATE HOSPICIOUS EWENT.

BY A GENTLEMAN OF THE FOOT-GUARDS (BLUE).

I PACED upon my beat
　　With steady step and slow,
All huppandownd of Ranelagh Street ;
　　Ran'lagh St. Pimlico.

While marching huppandownd
　　Upon that fair May morn,
Beold the booming cannings sound,
　　A royal child is born !

The Ministers of State
　　Then presnly I sor,
They gallops to the Pallis gate,
　　In carridges and for.

With anxious looks intent,
　　Before the gate they stop,
There comes the good Lord President,
　　And there the Archbishopp.

Lord John he next elights ;
　　And who comes here in haste ?
'Tis the ero of one underd fights,
　　The caudle for to taste.

Then Mrs. Lily, the nuss,
　　Towards them steps with joy ;
Says the brave old Duke, " Come tell to us,
　　Is it a gal or a boy ? "

* The birth of Prince Arthur.

Says Mrs. L. to the Duke,
  "Your Grace, it is *a Prince.*"
And at that nuss's bold rebuke
  He did both laugh and wince.

He vews with pleasant look
  This pooty flower of May,
Then says the wenerable Duke,
  "Egad, it's my buthday."

By memory backards borne,
  Peraps his thoughts did stray
To that old place where he was born
  Upon the first of May.

Perhaps he did recal
  The ancient towers of Trim ;
And County Meath and Dangan Hall
  They did rewisit him.

I phansy of him so
  His good old thoughts employin' ;
Fourscore years and one ago
  Beside the flowin' Boyne.

His father praps he sees,
  Most musicle of Lords,
A playing maddrigles and glees
  Upon the Arpsicords.

Jest phansy this old Ero
  Upon his mother's knee !
Did ever lady in this land
  Ave greater sons than she ?

And I shoudn be surprize
  While this was in his mind,
If a drop there twinkled in his eyes
  Of unfamiliar brind.

To Hapsly Ouse next day
  Drives up a Broosh and for,
A gracious prince sits in that Shay
  (I mention him with Hor !)

They ring upon the bell,
  The Porter shows his Ed,
(He fought at Vaterloo as vell,
  And vears a Veskit red).

To see that carriage come,
  The people round it press :
" And is the galliant Duke at ome ?"
  " Your Royal Ighness, yes."

He stepps from out the Broosh
  And in the gate is gone ;
And X, although the people push,
  Says wery kind, " Move hon."

The Royal Prince unto
  The galliant Duke did say,
" Dear Duke, my little son and you
  Was born the self same day.

" The Lady of the land,
  My wife and Sovring dear,
It is by her horgust command
  I wait upon you here.

" That lady is as well
  As can expected be ;
And to your Grace she bid me tel
  This gracious message free.

" That offspring of our race,
  Whom yesterday you see,
To show our honour for your Grace,
  Prince Arthur he shall be.

" That name it rhymes to fame ;
  All Europe knows the sound :
And I couldn't find a better name
  If you'd give me twenty pound.

" King Arthur had his knights
  That girt his table round,
But you have won a hundred fights,
  Will match 'em, I'll be bound.

" You fought with Bonypart,
  And likewise Tippoo Saib ;
I name you then with all my heart
  The Godsire of this babe."

That Prince his leave was took,
  His hinterview was done.
So let us give the good old Duke
  Good luck of his god-son,

And wish him years of joy
  In this our time of Schism,
And hope he'll hear the royal boy
  His little catechism.

And my pooty little Prince
  That's come our arts to cheer,
Let me my loyal powers ewince
  A welcomin of you ere.

And the Poit-Laureat's crownd,
  I think, in some respex,
Egstremely shootable might be found
  For honest Pleaseman X.

THE BALLAD OF ELIZA DAVIS.

GALLIANT gents and lovely ladies,
   List a tail vich late befel,
Vich I heard it, bein on duty,
   At the Pleace Hoffice, Clerkenwell.

Praps you know the Fondling Chapel,
   Vere the little children sings :
(Lor ! I likes to hear on Sundies
   Them there pooty little things !)

In this street there lived a housemaid,
  If you particklarly ask me where—
Vy, it vas at four-and-tventy
  Guilford Street, by Brunsvick Square.

Vich her name was Eliza Davis,
  And she went to fetch the beer :
In the street she met a party
  As was quite surprized to see her.

Vich he vas a British Sailor,
  For to judge him by his look :
Tarry jacket, canvass trowsies,
  Ha-la Mr. T. P. Cooke.

Presently this Mann accostes
  Of this hinnocent young gal—
" Pray," saysee, " excuse my freedom,
  You're so like my Sister Sal !

" You're so like my Sister Sally,
  Both in valk and face and size,
Miss, that—dang my old lee scuppers,
  It brings tears into my heyes !

" I'm a mate on board a wessel,
  I'm a sailor bold and true ;
Shiver up my poor old timbers,
  Let me be a mate for you !

" What's your name, my beauty, tell me ; "
  And she faintly hansers, " Lore,
Sir, my name's Eliza Davis,
  And I live at tventy-four."

Hofttimes came this British seaman,
  This deluded gal to meet ;
And at tventy-four was welcome,
  Tventy-four in Guilford Street.

And Eliza told her Master
  (Kinder they than Missuses are),
How in marridge he had ast her,
  Like a galliant Brittish Tar.

And he brought his landlady vith him,
  (Vich vas all his hartful plan),
And she told how Charley Thompson
  Reely vas a good young man ;

And how she herself had lived in
  Many years of union sweet
Vith a gent she met promiskous,
  Valkin in the public street.

And Eliza listened to them,
  And she thought that soon their bands
Vould be published at the Fondlin,
  Hand the clergyman jine their ands.

And he ast about the lodgers,
  (Vich her master let some rooms),
Likevise vere they kep their things, and
  Vere her master kep his spoons.

Hand this vicked Charley Thompson
  Came on Sundy veek to see her ;
And he sent Eliza Davis
  Hout to fetch a pint of beer.

Hand while pore Eliza vent to
  Fetch the beer, dewoid of sin,
This etrocious Charley Thompson
  Let his wile accomplish hin.

To the lodgers, their apartments,
  This abandingd female goes,
Prigs their shirts and umberellas ;
  Prigs their boots, and hats, and clothes.

Vile the scoundrle Charley Thompson,
　　Lest his wictim should escape,
Hocust her vith rum and vater,
　　Like a fiend in huming shape.

But a hi was fixt upon 'em
　　Vich these raskles little sore ;
Namely, Mr. Hide, the landlord
　　Of the house at tventy-four.

He vas valkin in his garden,
　　Just afore he vent to sup ;
And on looking up he sor the
　　Lodgers' vinders lighted hup.

Hup the stairs the landlord tumbled ;
　　Something's going wrong, he said ;
And he caught the vicked voman
　　Underneath the lodgers' bed.

And he called a brother Pleaseman,
　　Vich vas passing on his beat,
Like a true and galliant feller,
　　Hup and down in Guilford Street.

And that Pleaseman able-bodied
　　Took this voman to the cell ;
To the cell vere she was quodded,
　　In the Close of Clerkenwell.

And though vicked Charley Thompson
　　Boulted like a miscrant base,
Presently another Pleaseman
　　Took him to the self-same place.

And this precious pair of raskles
　　Tuesday last came up for doom ;
By the beak they was committed,
　　Vich his name was Mr. Combe.

Has for poor Eliza Davis,
　　Simple gurl of tventy-four,
She, I ope, vill never listen
　　In the streets to sailors moar.

But if she must ave a sweet-art,
　　(Vich most every gurl expex,)
Let her take a jolly pleaseman ;
　　Vich his name peraps is—X.

DAMAGES, TWO HUNDRED POUNDS.

SPECIAL Jurymen of England ! who admire your country's laws,
And proclaim a British Jury worthy of the realm's applause ;
Gaily compliment each other at the issue of a cause
Which was tried at Guildford 'sizes this day week as ever was.

Unto that august tribunal comes a gentleman in grief,
(Special was the British Jury, and the Judge, the Baron Chief,)
Comes a British man and husband—asking of the law relief,
For his wife was stolen from him—he'd have vengeance on the thief.

Yes, his wife, the blessed treasure with the which his life was
    crowned,
Wickedly was ravished from him by a hypocrite profound.
And he comes before twelve Britons, men for sense and truth
    renowned,
To award him for his damage twenty hundred sterling pound.

He by counsel and attorney there at Guildford does appear,
Asking damage of the villain who seduced his lady dear :
But I can't help asking, though the lady's guilt was all too clear,
And though guilty the defendant, wasn't the plaintiff rather queer ?

First the lady's mother spoke, and said she'd seen her daughter cry
But a fortnight after marriage : early times for piping eye.
Six months after, things were worse, and the piping eye was black,
And this gallant British husband caned his wife upon the back.

Three months after they were married, husband pushed her to the
    door,
Told her to be off and leave him, for he wanted her no more.
As she would not go, why *he* went : thrice he left his lady dear ;
Left her, too, without a penny, for more than a quarter of a year.

Mrs. Frances Duncan knew the parties very well indeed,
She had seen him pull his lady's nose and make her lip to bleed ;
If he chanced to sit at home not a single word he said :
Once she saw him throw the cover of a dish at his lady's head.

Sarah Green, another witness, clear did to the jury note
How she saw this honest fellow seize his lady by the throat,
How he cursed her and abused her, beating her into a fit,
Till the pitying next-door neighbours crossed the wall and
    witnessed it.

Next door to this injured Briton Mr. Owers a butcher dwelt ;
Mrs. Owers's foolish heart towards this erring dame did melt ;
(Not that she had erred as yet, crime was not developed in her),
But being left without a penny, Mrs. Owers supplied her dinner—
God be merciful to Mrs. Owers, who was merciful to this sinner !

Caroline Naylor was their servant, said they led a wretched life,
Saw this most distinguished Briton fling a teacup at his wife ;
He went out to balls and pleasures, and never once, in ten months'
    space,
Sat with his wife or spoke her kindly.   This was the defendant's case.

Pollock, C.B., charged the Jury ; said the woman's guilt was clear :
That was not the point, however, which the Jury came to hear ;
But the damage to determine which, as it should true appear,
This most tender-hearted husband, who so used his lady dear—

Beat her, kicked her, caned her, cursed her, left her starving, year
    by year,
Flung her from him, parted from her, wrung her neck, and boxed
    her ear—
What the reasonable damage this afflicted man could claim
By the loss of the affections of this guilty graceless dame ?

Then the honest British Twelve, to each other turning round,
Laid their clever heads together with a wisdom most profound :
And towards his Lordship looking, spoke the foreman wise and
    sound ;—
'My Lord, we find for this here plaintiff, damages two hundred
    pound."

So, God bless the Special Jury! pride and joy of English ground,
And the happy land of England, where true justice does abound !
British jurymen and husbands, let us hail this verdict proper:
If a British wife offends you, Britons, you've a right to whop her.

Though you promised to protect her, though you promised to
    defend her,
You are welcome to neglect her : to the devil you may send her:
You may strike her, curse, abuse her ; so declares our law
    renowned ;
And if after this you lose her,—why, you're paid two hundred pound

THE KNIGHT AND THE LADY.

THERE'S in the Vest a city pleasant
  To vich King Bladud gev his name,
And in that city there's a Crescent
  Vere dwelt a noble knight of fame.

Although that galliant knight is oldish,
  Although Sir John as grey, grey air,
Hage has not made his busum coldish,
  His Art still beats tewodds the Fair !

'Twas two years sins, this knight so splendid,
  Peraps fateagued with Bath's routines,

To Paris towne his phootsteps bended
   In sutch of gayer folks and seans.

His and was free, his means was easy,
   A nobler, finer gent than he
Ne'er drove about the Shons-Eleesy,
   Or paced the Roo de Rivolee.

A brougham and pair Sir John prowided,
   In which abroad he loved to ride ;
But ar ! he most of all enjyed it,
   When some one helse was sittin' inside !

That " some one helse " a lovely dame was,
   Dear ladies, you will heasy tell—
Countess Grabrowski her sweet name was,
   A noble title, ard to spell.

This faymus Countess ad a daughter
   Of lovely form and tender art;
A nobleman in marridge sought her,
   By name the Baron of Saint Bart.

Their pashn touched the noble Sir John,
   It was so pewer and profound ;
Lady Grabrowski he did urge on
   With Hyming's wreeth their loves to crownd.

" O, come to Bath, to Lansdowne Crescent,"
   Says kind Sir John, " and live with me ;
The living there's uncommon pleasant—
   I'm sure you'll find the hair agree.

" O, come to Bath, my fair Grabrowski,
   And bring your charming girl," sezee ;
" The Barring here shall have the ouse-key,
   Vith breakfast, dinner, lunch, and tea.

"And when they've passed an appy winter,
    Their opes and loves no more we'll bar;
The marridge-vow they'll enter inter,
    And I at church will be their Par."

To Bath they went to Lansdowne Crescent,
    Where good Sir John he did provide
No end of teas and balls incessant,
    And hosses both to drive and ride.

He was so Ospitably busy,
    When Miss was late, he'd make so bold
Upstairs to call out, " Missy, Missy,
    Come down, the coffy's getting cold !"

But O ! 'tis sadd to think such bounties
    Should meet with such return as this;
O Barring of Saint Bart, O Countess
    Grabrowski, and O cruel Miss !

He married you at Bath's fair Habby,
    Saint Bart he treated like a son—
And wasn't it uncommon shabby
    To do what you have went and done !

My trembling And amost refewses
    To write the charge which Sir John swore,
Of which the Countess he ecuses,
    Her daughter and her son-in-lore.

My Mews quite blushes as she sings of
    The fatle charge which now I quote:
He says Miss took his two best rings off,
    And pawned 'em for a tenpun note.

"Is this the child of honest parince,
    To make away with folks' best things ?

Is this, pray, like the wives of Barrins,
  To go and prig a gentleman's rings?"

Thus thought Sir John, by anger wrought on,
  And to rewenge his injured cause,
He brought them hup to Mr. Broughton,
  Last Vensday veek as ever waws.

If guiltless, how she have been slandered!
  If guilty, wengeance will not fail:
Meanwhile the lady is remanded
  And gev three hundred pouns in bail.

JACOB HOMNIUM'S HOSS.

A NEW PALLICE COURT CHAUNT.

ONE sees in Viteall Yard,
  Vere pleacemen do resort,
A wenerable hinstitute,
  'Tis called the Pallis Court.
A gent as got his i on it,
  I think 'twill make some sport.

The natur of this Court
  My hindignation riles:
A few fat legal spiders
  Here set & spin their viles;
To rob the town theyr privlege is,
  In a hayrea of twelve miles.

The Judge of this year Court
  Is a mellitary beak,
He knows no more of Lor
  Than praps he does of Greek,
And prowides hisself a deputy
  Because he cannot speak.

Four counsel in this Court—
  Misnamed of Justice—sits ;
These lawyers owes their places to
  Their money, not their wits ;
And there's six attornies under them,
  As here their living gits.

These lawyers, six and four,
  Was a livin at their ease,
A sendin of their writs abowt,
  And droring in the fees,
When their erose a cirkimstance
  As is like to make a breeze.

It now is some monce since
  A gent both good and trew
Possest an ansum oss vith vich
  He didn know what to do ;
Peraps he did not like the oss,
  Peraps he was a scru.

This gentleman his oss
  At Tattersall's did lodge ;
There came a wulgar oss-dealer,
  This gentleman's name did fodge,
And took the oss from Tattersall's :
  Wasn that a artful dodge ?

One day this gentleman's groom
  This willain did spy out,
A mounted on this oss
  A ridin him about ;
" Get out of that there oss, you rogue,"
  Speaks up the groom so stout.

The thief was cruel whex'd
  To find himself so pinn'd ;
The oss began to whinny,
  The honest groom he grinn'd ;
And the raskle thief got off the oss
  And cut avay like vind.

And phansy with what joy
  The master did regard
His dearly bluvd lost oss again
  Trot in the stable yard !

Who was this master good
  Of whomb I makes these rhymes ?
His name is Jacob Homnium, Exquire ;
  And if *I*'d committed crimes,
Good Lord ! I wouldn't ave that mann
  Attack me in the *Times!*

Now shortly after the groomb
  His master's oss did take up,
There came a livery-man
  This gentleman to wake up ;
And he handed in a little bill,
  Which hangered Mr. Jacob.

For two pound seventeen
  This livery-man eplied,
For the keep of Mr. Jacob's oss,
  Which the thief had took to ride.
" Do you see anythink green in me ? "
  Mr. Jacob Homnium cried.

"Because a raskle chews
  My oss away to robb,
And goes tick at your Mews
  For seven-and-fifty bobb,
Shall *I* be call'd to pay ?—It is
  A iniquitious Jobb."

Thus Mr. Jacob cut
  The conwasation short ;
The livery-man went ome,
  Detummingd to ave sport,
And summingsd Jacob Homnium, Exquire,
  Into the Pallis Court.

Pore Jacob went to Court,
   A Counsel for to fix,
And choose a barrister out of the four,
   An attorney of the six:
And there he sor these men of Lor,
   And watch'd 'em at their tricks.

The dreadful day of trile
   In the Pallis Court did come;
The lawyers said their say,
   The Judge look'd wery glum,
And then the British Jury cast
   Pore Jacob Hom-ni-um.

O a weary day was that
   For Jacob to go through;
The debt was two seventeen
   (Which he no mor owed than you),
And then there was the plaintives costs,
   Eleven pound six and two.

And then there was his own,
   Which the lawyers they did fix
At the wery moderit figgar
   Of ten pound one and six.
Now Evins bless the Pallis Court,
   And all its bold ver-dicks !

I cannot settingly tell
   If Jacob swaw and cust,
At aving for to pay this sumb ;
   But I should think he must,
And av drawn a cheque for £24 4s. 8d.
   With most igstreme disgust.

O Pallis Court, you move
   My pitty most profound.
A most emusing sport
   You thought it, I'll be bound,
To saddle hup a three-pound debt
   With two-and-twenty pound.

Good sport it is to you
　　To grind the honest pore,
To pay their just or unjust debts
　　With eight hundred per cent. for Lor ;
Make haste and get your costes in,
　　They will not last much mor !

Come·down from that tribewn,
　　Thou shameless and Unjust ;
Thou Swindle, picking pockets in
　　The name of Truth august :
Come down, thou hoary Blasphemy,
　　For die thou shalt and must.

And go it, Jacob Homnium,
　　And ply your iron pen,
And rise up, Sir John Jervis,
　　And shut me up that den ;
That sty for fattening lawyers in
　　On the bones of honest men.

　　　　　　　　PLEACEMAN **X.**

THE SPECULATORS.

THE night was stormy and dark,   The town was shut up in sleep:
Only those were abroad who were out on a lark,   Or those who'd no
beds to keep.

I pass'd through the lonely street,   The wind did sing and blow;
I could hear the policeman's feet   Clapping to and fro.

There stood a potato-man   In the midst of all the wet;   He stood
with his 'tato can   In the lonely Haymarket.

Two gents of dismal mien, And dank and greasy rags, Came out of a shop for gin, Swaggering over the flags :

Swaggering over the stones, These shabby bucks did walk ; And I went and followed those seedy ones, And listened to their talk.

Was I sober or awake ? Could I believe my ears ? Those dismal beggars spake Of nothing but railroad shares.

I wondered more and more : Says one—" Good friend of mine, How many shares have you wrote for, In the Diddlesex Junction line ? "

" I wrote for twenty," says Jim, " But they wouldn't give me one ; " His comrade straight rebuked him For the folly he had done :

" O Jim, you are unawares Of the ways of this bad town ; *I* always write for five hundred shares, And *then* they put me down."

" And yet you got no shares," Says Jim, "for all your boast ; " " I *would* have wrote," says Jack, " but where Was the penny to pay the post ? "

" I lost, for I couldn't pay That first instalment up ; But here's taters smoking hot—I say, Let's stop, my boy, and sup."

And at this simple feast The while they did regale, I drew each ragged capitalist Down on my left thumb-nail.

Their talk did me perplex, All night I tumbled and tost, And thought of railroad specs, And how money was won and lost.

" Bless railroads everywhere," I said, "and the world's advance ; Bless every railroad share In Italy, Ireland, France ; For never a beggar need now despair, And every rogue has a chance."

A WOEFUL NEW BALLAD

OF THE

PROTESTANT CONSPIRACY TO TAKE THE POPE'S LIFE.

BY A GENTLEMAN WHO HAS BEEN ON THE SPOT.)

COME all ye Christian people, unto my tale give ear,
'Tis about a base consperracy, as quickly shall appear ;
'Twill make your hair to bristle up, and your eyes to start and glow,
When of this dread consperracy you honest folks shall know.

The news of this consperracy and villianous attempt,
I read it in a newspaper, from Italy it was sent :
It was sent from lovely Italy, where the olives they do grow,
And our Holy Father lives, yes, yes, while his name it is NO NO.

And 'tis there our English noblemen goes that is Puseyites no longer,
Because they finds the ancient faith both better is and stronger.
And 'tis there I knelt beside my lord when he kiss'd the POPE his toe,
And hung his neck with chains at Saint Peter's Vinculo.

And 'tis there the splendid churches is, and the fountains playing
        grand,
And the palace of PRINCE TORLONIA, likewise the Vatican ;
And there's the stairs where the bagpipe-men and the piffararys blow.
And it's there I drove my lady and lord in the Park of Pincio.

And 'tis there our splendid churches is in all their pride and glory,
Saint Peter's famous Basilisk and Saint Mary's Maggiory ;
And them benighted Prodestants, on Sunday they must go
Outside the town to the preaching-shop by the gate of Popolo.

Now in this town of famous Room, as I dessay you have heard,
There is scarcely any gentleman as hasn't got a beard.
And ever since the world began it was ordained so,
That there should always barbers be wheresumever beards do grow.

And as it always has been so since the world it did begin,
The POPE, our Holy Potentate, has a beard upon his chin ;
And every morning regular when cocks begin to crow,
There comes a certing party to wait on POPE PIO.

There comes a certing gintleman with razier, soap, and lather,
A shaving most respectfully the POPE, our Holy Father.
And now the dread consperracy I'll quickly to you show,
Which them sanguinary Prodestants did form against NONO.

Them sanguinary Prodestants, which I abore and hate,
Assembled in the preaching-shop by the Flaminian gate ;
And they took counsel with their selves to deal a deadly blow
Against our gentle Father, the Holy POPE PIO.

Exhibiting a wickedness which I never heerd or read of ;
What do you think them Prodestants wished? to cut the good Pope's
    head off !
And to the kind POPE'S Air-dresser the Prodestant Clark did go,
And proposed him to decapitate the innocent PIO.

"What hever can be easier," said this Clerk—this Man of Sin,
"When you are called to hoperate on His Holiness's chin,
Than just to give the razier a little slip—just so ?—
And there's an end, dear barber, of innocent PIO ! "

This wicked conversation it chanced was overerd
By an Italian lady ; she heard it every word :
Which by birth she was a Marchioness, in service forced to go
With the parson of the preaching-shop at the gate of Popolo.

When the lady heard the news, as duty did obleege,
As fast as her legs could carry her she ran to the Poleege.
"O Polegia," says she (for they pronounts it so),
" They're going for to massyker our Holy POPE PIO.

" The ebomminable Englishmen, the Parsing and his Clark,
His Holiness's Air-dresser devised it in the dark !
And I would recommend you in prison for to throw
These villians would esassinate the Holy POPE PIO !

" And for saving of His Holiness and his trebble crownd
I humbly hope your Worships will give me a few pound ;
Because I was a Marchioness many years ago,
Before I came to service at the gate of Popolo."

That sackreligious Air-dresser, the Parson and his man,
Wouldn't, though ask'd continyally, own their wicked plan—
And so the kind Authoraties let those villians go
That was plotting of the murder of the good PIO NONO.

Now isn't this safishnt proof, ye gentlemen at home,
How wicked is them Prodestants, and how good our Pope at Rome ;
So let us drink confusion to LORD JOHN and LORD MINTO,
And a health unto His Eminence, and good PIO NONO.

THE LAMENTABLE BALLAD OF THE
FOUNDLING OF SHOREDITCH.

COME all ye Christian people, and listen to my tail,
It is all about a doctor was travelling by the rail,
By the Heastern Counties' Railway (vich the shares I don't desire),
From Ixworth town in Suffolk, vich his name did not transpire.

A travelling from Bury this Doctor was employed
With a gentleman, a friend of his, vich his name was Captain Loyd,
And on reaching Marks Tey Station, that is next beyond Colchester, a lady entered in to them most elegantly dressed.

She entered into the Carriage all with a tottering step,
And a pooty little Bayby upon her bussum slep ;
The gentlemen received her with kindness and siwillaty,
Pitying this lady for her illness and debillaty.

She had a fust-class ticket, this lovely lady said ;
Because it was so lonesome she took a secknd instead.
Better to travel by secknd class, than sit alone in the fust,
And the pooty little Baby upon her breast she nust.

A seein of her cryin, and shiverin and pail,
To her spoke this surging, the Ero of my tail ;
Saysee you look unwell, Ma'am, I'll elp you if I can,
And you may tell your case to me, for I'm a meddicle man.

" Thank you, Sir," the lady said, " I only look so pale,
Because I ain't accustom'd to travelling on the Rale ;
I shall be better presnly, when I've ad some rest : "
And that pooty little Baby she squeeged it to her breast.

So in conwersation the journey they beguiled,
Capting Loyd and the meddicle man, and the lady and the child,
Till the warious stations along the line was passed,
For even the Heastern Counties' trains must come in at last.

When at Shoreditch turmminus at lenth stopped the train,
This kind meddicle gentleman proposed his aid again.
" Thank you, Sir," the lady said, " for your kyindness dear ;
My carridge and my osses is probibbly come here.

" Will you old this baby, please, vilst I step and see ? "
The Doctor was a famly man : " That I will," says he.
Then the little child she kist, kist it very gently,
Vich was sucking his little fist, sleeping innocently.

With a sigh from her art, as though she would have bust it,
Then she gave the Doctor the child—wery kind he nust it :
Hup then the lady jumped hoff the bench she sat from,
Tumbled down the carridge steps and ran along the platform.

Vile hall the other passengers vent upon their vays,
The Capting and the Doctor sat there in a maze ;
Some vent in a Homminibus, some vent in a Cabby,
The Capting and the Doctor vaited vith the babby.

There they sat looking queer, for an hour or more,
But their feller passinger neather on 'em sore :
Never, never back again did that lady come
To that pooty sleeping Hinfnt a suckin of his Thum !

What could this pore Doctor do, bein treated thus,
When the darling Baby woke, cryin for its nuss ?
Off he drove to a female friend, vich she was both kind and mild,
And igsplained to her the circumstance of this year little child.

That kind lady took the child instantly in her lap,
And made it very comfortable by giving it some pap ;
And when she took its close off, what d'you think she found ?
A couple of ten pun notes sewn up, in its little gownd !

Also in its little close, was a note which did conwey,
That this little baby's parents lived in a handsome way
And for its Headucation they reglarly would pay,
And sirtingly like gentlefolks would claim the child one day,
If the Christian people who'd charge of it would say,
Per adwertisement in *The Times*, where the baby lay.

Pity of this bayby many people took,
It had such pooty ways and such a pooty look ;
And there came a lady forrard (I wish that I could see
Any kind lady as would do as much for me ;

And I wish with all my art, some night in *my* night gownd,
I could find a note stitched for ten or twenty pound)—
There came a lady forrard, that most honorable did say,
She'd adopt this little baby, which her parents cast away.

While the Doctor pondered on this hoffer fair,
Comes a letter from Devonshire, from a party there,
Hordering the Doctor, at its Mar's desire,
To send the little Infant back to Devonshire.

Lost in apoplexity, this pore meddicle man,
Like a sensable gentleman, to the Justice ran ;
Which his name was Mr. Hammill, a honorable beak,
That takes his seat in Worship Street four times a week.

" O Justice ! " says the Doctor, "instrugt me what to do.
I've come up from the country, to throw myself on you ;
My patients have no doctor to tend them in their ills,
(There they are in Suffolk without their draffts and pills !)

" I've come up from the country, to know how I'll dispose
Of this pore little baby, and the twenty pun note, and the close,
And I want to go back to Suffolk, dear Justice, if you please,
And my patients wants their Doctor, and their Doctor wants his feez.

Up spoke Mr. Hammill, sittin at his desk,
" This year application does me much perplesk ;
What I do adwise you, is to leave this babby
In the Parish where it was left by its mother shabby."

The Doctor from his Worship sadly did depart—
He might have left the baby, but he hadn't got the heart
To go for to leave that Hinnocent, has the laws allows,
To the tender mussies of the Union House.

Mother, who left this little one on a stranger's knee,
Think how cruel you have been, and how good was he !
Think, if you've been guilty, innocent was she ;
And do not take unkindly this little word of me :
Heaven be merciful to us all, sinners as we be !

THE ORGAN-BOY'S APPEAL.

"WESTMINSTER POLICE COURT.—POLICEMAN X brought a paper of doggerel verses to the MAGISTRATE, which had been thrust into his hands, X said, by an Italian boy, who ran away immediately afterwards.

" The MAGISTRATE, after perusing the lines, looked hard at X, and said he did not think they were written by an Italian.

"X, blushing, said he thought the paper read in Court last week, and which frightened so the old gentleman to whom it was addressed, was also not of Italian origin."

O SIGNOR BRODERIP, you are a wickid ole man,
You wexis us little horgin-boys whenever you can :
How dare you talk of Justice, and go for to seek
To pussicute us horgin-boys, you senguinary Beek ?

Though you set in Vestminster surrounded by your crushers,
Harrogint and habsolute like the Hortacrat of hall the Rushers,
Yet there is a better vurld I'd have you for to know,
Likewise a place vere the henimies of horgin-boys will go.

O you vickid HEROD without any pity !
London vithout horgin-boys vood be a dismal city.
Sweet SAINT CICILY who first taught horgin-pipes to blow
Soften the heart of this Magistrit that haggerywates us so !

Good Italian gentlemen, fatherly and kind,
Brings us over to London here our horgins for to grind ;
Sends us out vith little vite mice and guinea-pigs also
A popping of the Veasel and a Jumpin of JIM CROW.

And as us young horgin-boys is grateful in our turn
We gives to these kind gentlemen hall the money we earn,
Because that they vood vop us as wery wel we know
Unless we brought our hurnings back to them as loves us so.

O MR. BRODERIP! wery much I'm surprise,
Ven you take your valks abroad where can be your eyes?
If a Beak had a heart then you'd compryend
Us pore little horgin-boys was the poor man's friend.

Don't you see the shildren in the droring-rooms
Clapping of their little ands when they year our toons?
On their mothers' bussums don't you see the babbies crow
And down to us dear horgin-boys lots of apence throw?

Don't you see the ousemaids (pooty POLLIES and MARIES),
Ven ve bring our urdigurdis, smiling from the hairies?
Then they come out vith a slice o' cole puddn or a bit o' bacon or so
And give it us young horgin-boys for lunch afore we go.

Have you ever seen the Hirish children sport
When our velcome music-box brings sunshine in the Court?
To these little paupers who can never pay
Surely all good horgin-boys, for GOD's love, will play.

Has for those proud gentlemen, like a serting B—k
(Vich I von't be pussonal and therefore vil not speak),
That flings their parler-vinders hup ven ve begin to play
And cusses us and swears at us in such a wiolent way,

Instedd of their abewsing and calling hout Poleece
Let em send out JOHN to us vith sixpence or a shillin apiece.
Then like good young horgin-boys away from there we'll go,
Blessing sweet SAINT CICILY that taught our pipes to blow.

THE

ROSE AND THE RING

OR THE

HISTORY OF PRINCE GIGLIO AND PRINCE BULBO

A Fire-side Pantomime for Great and Small Children

BY MR. M. A. TITMARSH

PRELUDE.

IT happened that the undersigned spent the last Christmas season in a foreign city where there were many English children.

In that city, if you wanted to give a child's party, you could not even get a magic-lantern or buy Twelfth-Night characters—those funny painted pictures of the King, the Queen, the Lover, the Lady, the Dandy, the Captain, and so on—with which our young ones are wont to recreate themselves at this festive time.

My friend Miss Bunch, who was governess of a large family that lived in the *Piano Nobile* of the house inhabited by myself and my young charges (it was the Palazzo Poniatowski at Rome, and Messrs. Spillmann, two of the best pastrycooks in Christendom, have their shop on the ground-floor) : Miss Bunch, I say, begged me to draw a set of Twelfth-Night characters for the amusement of our young people.

She is a lady of great fancy and droll imagination, and having looked at the characters, she and I composed a history about them, which was recited to the little folks at night, and served as our FIRE-SIDE PANTOMIME.

Our juvenile audience was amused by the adventures of Giglio and Bulbo, Rosalba and Angelica. I am bound to say the fate of the Hall Porter created a considerable sensation ; and the wrath of Countess Gruffanuff was received with extreme pleasure.

If these children are pleased, thought I, why should not others be amused also? In a few days Dr. Birch's young friends will be expected to re-assemble at Rodwell Regis, where they will learn everything that is useful, and under the eyes of careful ushers continue the business of their little lives.

But, in the meanwhile, and for a brief holiday, let us laugh and be as pleasant as we can. And you elder folks—a little joking, and dancing, and fooling will do even you no harm. The author wishes you a merry Christmas, and welcomes you to the Fire-side Pantomime.

M. A. TITMARSH.

December, 1854.

THE ROSE AND THE RING.

I.

SHOWS HOW THE ROYAL FAMILY SATE DOWN TO BREAKFAST.

THIS is Valoroso XXIV., King of Paflagonia, seated with his Queen and only child at their royal breakfast-table, and re-ceiving the letter which announces to his Majesty a proposed visit from Prince Bulbo, heir of Padella, reigning King of Crim Tartary. Remark the delight upon the monarch's royal features. He is so absorbed in the perusal of the King of Crim Tartary's letter, that he allows his eggs to get cold, and leaves his august muffins untasted.

"What! that wicked, brave, delightful Prince Bulbo!" cries Princess Angelica; "so handsome, so accomplished, so witty—the conqueror of Rimbombamento, where he slew ten thousand giants!"

"Who told you of him, my dear?" asks his Majesty.

"A little bird," says Angelica.

"Poor Giglio?" says mamma, pouring out the tea.

"Bother Giglio!" cries Angelica, tossing up her head, which rustled with a thousand curl-papers.

"I wish," growls the King—"I wish Giglio was . . ."

"Was better? Yes, dear, he is better," says the Queen. "Angelica's little maid, Betsinda, told me so when she came to my room this morning with my early tea."

"You are always drinking tea," said the Monarch, with a scowl.

"It is better than drinking port or brandy-and-water," replies her Majesty.

"Well, well, my dear, I only said you were fond of drinking tea," said the King of Paflagonia, with an effort as if to command his temper. "Angelica! I hope you have plenty of new dresses; your milliners' bills are long enough. My dear Queen, you must see and have some parties. I prefer dinners, but of course you will be for balls. Your everlasting blue velvet quite tires me: and, my love, I should like you to have a new necklace. Order one. Not more than a hundred or a hundred and fifty thousand pounds."

"And Giglio, dear," says the Queen.

"Giglio may go to the ——"

"Oh, sir," screams her Majesty. "Your own nephew! our late King's only son."

"Giglio may go to the tailor's, and order the bills to be sent in to Glumboso to pay. Confound him! I mean bless his dear heart. He need want for nothing; give him a couple of guineas for pocket money, my dear; and you may as well order yourself bracelets while you are about the necklace, Mrs. V."

Her Majesty, or *Mrs. V.*, as the monarch facetiously called her (for even royalty will have its sport, and this august family were very much attached), embraced her husband, and, twining her arm round her daughter's waist, they quitted the breakfast-room in order to make all things ready for the princely stranger.

When they were gone, the smile that had lighted up the eyes

the *husband* and *father* fled—the pride of the *King* fled—the MAN was alone. Had I the pen of a G. P. R. James, I would describe Valoroso's torments in the choicest language; in which I would also depict his flashing eye, his distended nostril—his dressing-gown, pocket-handkerchief, and boots. But I need not say I have *not* the pen of that novelist; suffice it to say, Valoroso was alone.

He rushed to the cupboard, seizing from the table one of the many egg-cups with which his princely board was served for the matin meal, drew out a bottle of right Nantz or Cognac, filled and emptied the cup several times, and laid it down with a hoarse " Ha, ha, ha ! now Valoroso is a man again."

" But oh ! " he went on (still sipping, I am sorry to say), " ere I was a king, I needed not this intoxicating draught ; once I detested the hot brandy wine, and quaffed no other fount but nature's rill. It dashes not more quickly o'er the rocks, than I did, as, with blunder-buss in hand, I brushed away the early morning dew, and shot the partridge, snipe, or antlered deer ! Ah ! well may England's dramatist remark, ' Uneasy lies the head that wears a crown ! ' Why did I steal my nephew's, my young Giglio's —— ? Steal ! said I? no, no, no, not steal, not steal. Let me withdraw that odious expression. I took, and on my manly head I set, the royal crown of Paflagonia ; I took, and with my royal arm I wield, the sceptral rod of Paflagonia; I took, and in my outstretched hand I hold, the royal orb of Paflagonia ! Could a poor boy, a snivelling, drivelling boy—was in his nurse's arms but yesterday, and cried for sugar-plums and puled for pap—bear up the awful weight of crown, orb, sceptre? gird on the sword my royal fathers wore, and meet in fight the tough Crimean foe? "

And then the monarch went on to argue in his own mind (though we need not say that blank verse is not argument) that what he had got it was his duty to keep, and that, if at one time he had entertained ideas of a certain restitution, which shall be nameless, the prospect by a *certain marriage* of uniting two crowns and two nations which had been engaged in bloody and expensive wars, as the Paflagonians and the Crimeans had been, put the idea of Giglio's restoration to the throne out of the question : nay, were his own brother, King Savio, alive, he would certainly will away the crown from his own son in order to bring about such a desirable union.

Thus easily do we deceive ourselves ! Thus do we fancy what we wish is right ! The King took courage, read the papers, finished his muffins and eggs, and rang the bell for his Prime Minister. The

Queen, after thinking whether she should go up and see Giglio, who had been sick, thought " Not now. Business first ; pleasure afterwards. I will go and see dear Giglio this afternoon ; and now I will drive to the jeweller's, to look for the necklace and bracelets." The Princess went up into her own room, and made Betsinda, her maid, bring out all her dresses ; and as for Giglio, they forgot him as much as I forget what I had for dinner last Tuesday twelvemonth.

II.

HOW KING VALOROSO GOT THE CROWN, AND PRINCE GIGLIO WENT WITHOUT.

PAFLAGONIA, ten or twenty thousand years ago, appears to have been one of those kingdoms where the laws of succession were not settled; for when King Savio died, leaving his brother Regent of the kingdom, and guardian of Savio's orphan infant, this unfaithful regent took no sort of regard of the late monarch's will; had himself proclaimed sovereign of Paflagonia under the title of King Valoroso XXIV., had a most splendid coronation, and ordered all the nobles of the kingdom to pay him homage. So long as Valoroso gave them plenty of balls at Court, plenty of money and lucrative places, the Paflagonian nobility did not care who was king; and, as for the people, in those early times they were equally indifferent. The Prince Giglio, by reason of his tender age at his royal father's death, did not feel the loss of his crown and empire. As long as he had plenty of toys and sweetmeats, a holiday five times a week, and a horse and gun to go out shooting when he grew a little older, and, above all, the company of his darling cousin, the King's only child, poor Giglio was perfectly contented; nor did he envy his uncle the royal robes and sceptre, the great hot uncomfortable throne of state, and the enormous cumbersome crown in which that monarch appeared from morning till night. King Valoroso's portrait has been left to us; and I think you will agree with me that he must have been sometimes *rather tired* of his velvet, and his diamonds, and his ermine, and his grandeur. I shouldn't like to sit in that stifling robe, with such a thing as that on my head.

No doubt, the Queen must have been lovely in her youth; for though she grew rather stout in after life, yet her features, as shown

in her portrait, are certainly *pleasing*. If she was fond of flatter scandal, cards, and fine clothes, let us deal gently with her infirmitie which, after all, may be no greater than our own. She was kind to her nephew; and if she had any scruples of conscience about her

husband's taking the young Prince's crown, consoled herself by thinking that the King, though a usurper, was a most respectable man, and that at his death Prince Giglio would be restored to his throne, and share it with his cousin, whom he loved so fondly.

The Prime Minister was Glumboso, an old statesman, who most cheerfully swore fidelity to King Valoroso, and in whose hands the monarch left all the affairs of his kingdom. All Valoroso wanted was plenty of money, plenty of hunting, plenty of flattery, and as little trouble as possible. As long as he had his sport, this monarch cared little how his people paid for it: he engaged in some wars, and of course the Paflagonian newspapers announced that he gained prodigious victories: he had statues erected to himself in every city of the empire; and of course his pictures placed everywhere, and in all the print-shops: he was Valoroso the Magnanimous, Valoroso the Victorious, Valoroso the Great, and so forth;—for even in these early times courtiers and people knew how to flatter.

This royal pair had one only child, the Princess Angelica, who, you may be sure, was a paragon in the courtiers' eyes, in her parents', and in her own. It was said she had the longest hair, the largest eyes, the slimmest waist, the smallest foot, and the most lovely complexion of any young lady in the Paflagonian dominions. Her accomplishments were announced to be even superior to her beauty; and governesses used to shame their idle pupils by telling them what Princess Angelica could do. She could play the most difficult pieces of music at sight. She could answer any one of *Mangnall's Questions.* She knew every date in the history of Paflagonia, and every other country. She knew French, English, Italian, German, Spanish, Hebrew, Greek, Latin, Cappadocian, Samothracian, Ægean, and Crim Tartar. In a word, she was a most accomplished young creature; and her governess and lady-in-waiting was the severe Countess Gruffanuff.

Would you not fancy, from this picture, that Gruffanuff must have been a person of the highest birth? She looks so haughty that I should have thought her a Princess at the very least, with a pedigree reaching as far back as the Deluge. But this lady was no better born than many other ladies who give themselves airs; and all sensible people laughed at her absurd pretensions.

The fact is, she had been maid-servant to the Queen when her Majesty was only Princess, and her husband had been head footman; but after his death or *disappearance*, of which you shall hear presently, this Mrs. Gruffanuff, by flattering, toadying, and wheedling her royal mistress, became a favourite with the Queen (who was rather a weak woman), and her Majesty gave her a title, and made her nursery governess to the Princess.

And now I must tell you about the Princess's learning and accomplishments, for which she had such a wonderful character. Clever

Angelica certainly was, but as *idle as possible.* Play at sight, indeed! she could play one or two pieces, and pretend that she had never seen them before; she could answer half-a-dozen *Mangnall's Questions;* but then you must take care to ask the *right* ones. As for her

languages, she had masters in plenty, but I doubt whether she knew more than a few phrases in each, for all her pretence ; and as for her embroidery and her drawing, she showed beautiful specimens, it is true, but *who did them ?*

This obliges me to tell the truth, and to do so I must go back ever so far, and tell you about the FAIRY BLACKSTICK.

III.

TELLS WHO THE FAIRY BLACKSTICK WAS, AND WHO WERE EVER
SO MANY GRAND PERSONAGES BESIDES.

BETWEEN the kingdoms of Paflagonia and Crim Tartary, there
lived a mysterious personage, who was known in those countries
as the Fairy Blackstick, from the ebony wand or crutch which she
carried ; on which she rode to the moon sometimes, or upon other
excursions of business or pleasure, and with which she performed her
wonders.

When she was young, and had been first taught the art of conjuring
by the necromancer, her father, she was always practising her skill,
whizzing about from one kingdom to another upon her black stick, and
conferring her fairy favours upon this Prince or that. She had scores
of royal godchildren ; turned numberless wicked people into beasts,
birds, millstones, clocks, pumps, bootjacks, umbrelias, or other absurd shapes ; and in a word was one of the most active and officious
of the whole College of fairies.

But after two or three thousand years of this sport, I suppose
Blackstick grew tired of it. Or perhaps she thought, "What good am
I doing by sending this Princess to sleep for a hundred years? by
fixing a black pudding on to that booby's nose ? by causing diamonds
and pearls to drop from one little girl's mouth, and vipers and toads
from another's ? I begin to think I do as much harm as good by my
performances. I might as well shut my incantations up, and allow
things to take their natural course.

" There were my two young goddaughters, King Savio's wife, and
Duke Padella's wife : I gave them each a present, which was to render

them charming in the eyes of their husbands, and secure the affection of those gentlemen as long as they lived. What good did my Rose and my Ring do these two women? None on earth. From having all their whims indulged by their husbands, they became capricious, lazy, ill-humoured, absurdly vain, and leered and languished, and fancied themselves irresistibly beautiful, when they were really quite old and hideous, the ridiculous creatures! They used actually to patronise me when I went to pay them a visit;—*me*, the Fairy Blackstick, who knows all the wisdom of the necromancers, and who could have turned them into baboons, and all their diamonds into strings of onions, by a single wave of my rod!" So she locked up her books in her cupboard, declined further magical performances, and scarcely used her wand at all except as a cane to walk about with.

So when Duke Padella's lady had a little son (the Duke was at that time only one of the principal noblemen in Crim Tartary), Blackstick, although invited to the christening, would not so much as attend; but merely sent her compliments and a silver papboat for the baby, which was really not worth a couple of guineas. About the same time the Queen of Paflagonia presented his Majesty with a son and heir; and guns were fired, the capital illuminated, and no end of feasts ordained to celebrate the young Prince's birth. It was thought the Fairy, who was asked to be his godmother, would at least have presented him with an invisible jacket, a flying horse, a Fortunatus's purse, or some other valuable token of her favour; but instead, Blackstick went up to the cradle of the child Giglio, when everybody was admiring him and complimenting his royal papa and mamma, and said,

"My poor child, the best thing I can send you is a little *misfortune;*" and this was all she would utter, to the disgust of Giglio's parents, who died very soon after, when Giglio's uncle took the throne as we read in Chapter I.

In like manner, when CAVOLFIORE, King of Crim Tartary, had a christening of his only child, ROSALBA, the Fairy Blackstick, who had been invited, was not more gracious than in Prince Giglio's case. Whilst everybody was expatiating over the beauty of the darling child and congratulating its parents, the Fairy Blackstick looked very sadly at the baby and its mother, and said,

"My good woman—(for the Fairy was very familiar, and no more minded a Queen than a washerwoman)—my good woman, these people who are following you will be the first to turn against you; and, a

for this little lady, the best thing I can wish her is a *little misfortune.*"
So she touched Rosalba with her black wand, looked severely at the
courtiers, motioned the Queen an adieu with her hand, and sailed
slowly up into the air out of window.

When she was gone, the Court people, who had been awed and
silent in her presence, began to speak.

"What an odious Fairy she is (they said)—a pretty Fairy, indeed!
Why, she went to the King of Paflagonia's christening, and pretended
to do all sorts of things for that family; and what has happened—the
Prince, her godson, has been turned off his throne by his uncle.
Would we allow our sweet Princess to be deprived of her rights by
any enemy? Never, never, never, never!"

And they all shouted in a chorus, "Never, never, never, never!"

Now, I should like to know, how did these fine courtiers show
their fidelity? One of King Cavolfiore's vassals, the Duke Padella
just mentioned, rebelled against the King, who went out to chastise
his rebellious subject.

"Any one rebel against our beloved and august Monarch!" cried
the courtiers; "any one resist *him?* Pooh! He is invincible,
irresistible. He will bring home Padella a prisoner, and tie him to
a donkey's tail, and drive him round the town, saying, 'This is the
way the great Cavolfiore treats rebels.'"

The King went forth to vanquish Padella; and the poor Queen,
who was a very timid, anxious creature, grew so frightened and ill,
that I am sorry to say she died; leaving injunctions with her ladies
to take care of the dear little Rosalba.—Of course they said they
would. Of course they vowed they would die rather than any harm
should happen to the Princess. At first the *Crim Tartar Court
Journal* stated that the King was obtaining great victories over the
audacious rebel: then it was announced that the troops of the
infamous Padella were in flight: then it was said that the royal
army would soon come up with the enemy, and then—then the news
came that King Cavolfiore was vanquished and slain by his Majesty,
King Padella the First!

At this news, half the courtiers ran off to pay their duty to the
conquering chief, and the other half ran away, laying hands on all
the best articles in the palace; and poor little Rosalba was left there
quite alone—quite alone; and she toddled from one room to another,
crying, "Countess! Duchess! (only she said 'Tountess, Duttess,'
not being able to speak plain) bring me my mutton sop; my Royal
Highness hungy! Tountess! Duttess!"

And she went from the private apartments into the throne-room and nobody was there;—and thence into the ball-room and nobody was there;—and thence into the pages' room and nobody was there;—and she toddled down the great staircase into the hall and nobody was there;—and the door was open, and she went into the court,

and into the garden, and thence into the wilderness, and thence into the forest where the wild beasts live, and was never heard any more!

A piece of her torn mantle and one of her shoes were found the wood in the mouths of two lioness's cubs, whom KING PADEL and a royal hunting party shot—for he was King now, and reigned over **Crim Tartary.**

"So the poor little Princess is done for," said he ; "well, what's done can't be helped. Gentlemen, let us go to luncheon !" And one of the courtiers took up the shoe and put it in his pocket. And there was an end of Rosalba !

IV.

HOW BLACKSTICK WAS NOT ASKED TO THE PRINCESS ANGELICA'S CHRISTENING.

WHEN the Princess Angelica was born, her parents not only did not ask the Fairy Blackstick to the christening party, but gave orders to their porter absolutely to refuse her if she called. This porter's name was Gruffanuff, and he had been selected for the post by their Royal Highnesses because he was a very tall fierce man, who could say "Not at home" to a tradesman or an unwelcome visitor with a rudeness which frightened most such persons away. He was the husband of that Countess whose picture we have just seen, and as long as they were together they quarrelled from morning till night. Now this fellow tried his rudeness once too often, as you shall hear. For the Fairy Blackstick coming to call upon the Prince and Princess, who were actually sitting at the open drawing-room window, Gruffanuff not only denied them, but made the most *odious vulgar sign* as he was going to slam the door in the Fairy's face "Git away, hold Blackstick!" said he. "I tell you, Master and Missis ain't at home to you:" and he was, as we have said, *going* to slam the door.

But the Fairy, with her wand, prevented the door being shut; and Gruffanuff came out again in a fury, swearing in the most abominable way, and asking the Fairy "whether she thought he was a going to stay at that there door hall day?"

"You *are* going to stay at that door all day and all night, and for many a long year," the Fairy said, very majestically; and Gruffanuff coming out of the door, straddling before it with his great calves

burst out laughing, and cried " Ha, ha, ha ! this *is* a good un !   Ha—
ah—what's this?   Let me   down—O—o—H'm !" and then   he   was
dumb !

For, as the Fairy waved her wand over him, he felt himself rising

f the ground, and fluttering up against the door, and then, as if a
rew ran into his stomach, he felt a dreadful pain there, and was
ned to the door; and then his arms flew up over his head;
d his legs, after writhing about wildly, twisted under his body; and

he felt cold, cold, growing over him, as if he was turning into metal; and he said, " O—o—H'm !" and could say no more, because he was dumb.

He *was* turned into metal ! He was, from being *brazen, brass !* He was neither more nor less than a knocker ! And there he was, nailed to the door in the blazing summer day, till he burned almost red-hot; and there he was, nailed to the door all the bitter winter nights, till his brass nose was dropping with icicles. And the postman came and rapped at him, and the vulgarest boy with a letter came and hit him up against the door. And the King and Queen (Princess

and Prince they were then) coming home from a walk that evening the King said, " Hullo, my dear ! you have had a new knocker put on the door. Why, it's rather like our Porter in the face ! What has become of that boozy vagabond?" And the housemaid came and scrubbed his nose with sand-paper; and once, when the Princess Angelica's little sister was born, he was tied up in an old kid glove and another night, some *larking* young men tried to wrench him off and put him to the most excruciating agony with a turnscrew. And then the Queen had a fancy to have the colour of the door altered and the painters dabbed him over the mouth and eyes, and nearly choked him, as they painted him pea-green. I warrant he had leisure to repent of having been rude to the Fairy Blackstick !

As for his wife, she did not miss him ; and as he was always guzzling beer at the public-house, and notoriously quarrelling with his wife, and in debt to the tradesmen, it was supposed he had run away from all these evils, and emigrated to Australia or America. And when the Prince and Princess chose to become King and Queen, they left their old house, and nobody thought of the Porter any more.

21.

x

V.

HOW PRINCESS ANGELICA TOOK A LITTLE MAID.

ONE day, when the Princess Angelica was quite a little girl, she was walking in the garden of the palace, with Mrs. Gruffanuff the governess, holding a parasol over her head, to keep her swee complexion from the freckles, and Angelica was carrying a bun, t feed the swans and ducks in the royal pond.

They had not reached the duck-pond, when there came toddlin up to them such a funny little girl! She had a great quantity of hai blowing about her chubby little cheeks, and looked as if she had no been washed or combed for ever so long. She wore a ragged bit of cloak, and had only one shoe on.

"You little wretch, who let you in here?" asked Gruffanuff.

"Dive me dat bun," said the little girl, "me vely hungry."

"Hungry! what is that?" asked Princess Angelica, and gave th child the bun.

"Oh, Princess!" says Gruffanuff, "how good, how kind, ho truly angelical you are! See, your Majesties," she said to the Ki and Queen, who now came up, along with their nephew, Prince Gigl "how kind the Princess is! She met this little dirty wretch in t garden—I can't tell how she came in here, or why the guards did n shoot her dead at the gate!—and the dear darling of a Princess h given her the whole of her bun!"

"I didn't want it," said Angelica.

"But you are a darling little angel all the same," says t governess.

"Yes; I know I am," said Angelica. "Dirty little girl, don't you think I am very pretty?" Indeed, she had on the finest of little dresses and hats; and, as her hair was carefully curled, she really looked very well.

"Oh, pooty, pooty!" says the little girl, capering about, laughing, and dancing, and munching her bun; and as she ate it she began to sing, "Oh, what fun to have a plum bun! how I wis it never was

done!" At which, and her funny accent, Angelica, Giglio, and the King and Queen began to laugh very merrily.

"I can dance as well as sing," says the little girl. "I can dance, and I can sing, and I can do all sorts of ting." And she ran to a flower-bed, and, pulling a few polyanthuses, rhododendrons, and other flowers, made herself a little wreath, and danced before the King and Queen so drolly and prettily, that everybody was delighted.

"Who was your mother—who were your relations, little girl?" said the Queen.

The little girl said, "Little lion was my brudder; great big lioness

my mudder; neber heard of any udder." And she capered away her one shoe, and everybody was exceedingly diverted.

So Angelica said to the Queen, "Mamma, my parrot flew aw

yesterday out of its cage, and I don't care any more for any of my toys; and I think this funny little dirty child will amuse me. I will take her home, and give her some of my old frocks."

"Oh, the generous darling!" says Gruffanuff.

"Which I have worn ever so many times, and am quite tired of," Angelica went on; "and she shall be my little maid. Will you come home with me, little dirty girl?"

The child clapped her hands, and said, "Go home with you—yes! You pooty Princess!—Have a nice dinner, and wear a new dress!"

And they all laughed again, and took home the child to the palace, where, when she was washed and combed, and had one of the Princess's frocks given to her, she looked as handsome as Angelica, almost. Not that Angelica ever thought so; for this little lady never imagined that anybody in the world could be as pretty, as good, or as clever as herself. In order that the little girl should not become too proud and conceited, Mrs. Gruffanuff took her old ragged mantle and one shoe, and put them into a glass box, with a card laid upon them, upon which was written, "These were the old clothes in which little BETSINDA was found when the great goodness and admirable kindness of her Royal Highness the Princess Angelica received this little outcast." And the date was added, and the box locked up.

For a while little Betsinda was a great favourite with the Princess, and she danced, and sang, and made her little rhymes, to amuse her mistress. But then the Princess got a monkey, and afterwards a little dog, and afterwards a doll, and did not care for Betsinda any more, who became very melancholy and quiet, and sang no more funny songs, because nobody cared to hear her. And then, as she grew older, she was made a little lady's-maid to the Princess; and though she had no wages, she worked and mended, and put Angelica's hair in papers, and was never cross when scolded, and was always eager to please her mistress, and was always up early and to bed late, and at hand when wanted, and in fact became a perfect little maid. So the two girls grew up, and, when the Princess came out, Betsinda was never tired of waiting on her; and made her dresses better than the best milliner, and was useful in a hundred ways. Whilst the Princess was having her masters, Betsinda would sit and watch them; and in this way she picked up a great deal of learning; for she was always awake, though her mistress was not, and listened to the wise professors when Angelica was yawning or thinking of the next ball. And when the dancing-master came, Betsinda learned along with Angelica; and when the music-master came, she watched him, and practised the

Princess's pieces when Angelica was away at balls and parties; and when the drawing-master came, she took note of all he said and did; and the same with French, Italian, and all other languages—she learned them from the teacher who came to Angelica. When the Princess was going out of an evening she would say, "My good Betsinda, you may as well finish what I have begun." "Yes, Miss," Betsinda would say, and sit down very cheerful, not to *finish* what Angelica began, but to *do* it.

For instance, the Princess would begin a head of a warrior, let us say, and when it was begun it was something like this—

But when it was done, the warrior was like this—

(only handsomer still if possible), and the Princess put her name to the drawing; and the Court and King and Queen, and above all po

Giglio, admired the picture of all things, and said, "Was there ever a genius like Angelica?" So, I am sorry to say, was it with the Princess's embroidery and other accomplishments; and Angelica actually believed that she did these things herself, and received all the flattery of the Court as if every word of it was true. Thus she began to think that there was no young woman in all the world equal to herself, and that no young man was good enough for her. As for Betsinda, as she heard none of these praises, she was not puffed up by them, and being a most grateful, good-natured girl, she was only too anxious to do everything which might give her mistress pleasure. Now you begin to perceive that Angelica had faults of her own, and was by no means such a wonder of wonders as people represented her Royal Highness to be.

VI.

HOW PRINCE GIGLIO BEHAVED HIMSELF.

A ND now let us speak about Prince Giglio, the nephew of the
reigning monarch of Paflagonia. It has already been stated, in
page 291, that as long as he had a smart coat to wear, a good horse to
ride, and money in his pocket, or rather to take out of his pocket, for
he was very good-natured, my young Prince did not care for the loss

of his crown and sceptre, being a thoughtless youth, not much inclined to politics or any kind of learning. So his tutor had a sinecure. Giglio would not learn classics or mathematics, and the Lord Chancellor of Paflagonia, SQUARETOSO, pulled a very long face because the prince could not be got to study the Paflagonian laws and constitution; but, on the other hand, the King's gamekeepers and huntsmen found the Prince an apt pupil; the dancing-master pro-

nounced that he was a most elegant and assiduous scholar; the First Lord of the Billiard Table gave the most flattering reports of the Prince's skill; so did the Groom of the Tennis Court; and as for the Captain of the Guard and Fencing Master, the *valiant* and *veteran* Count KUTASOFF HEDZOFF, he avowed that since he ran the General of Crim Tartary, the dreadful Grumbuskin, through the body, he never had encountered so expert a swordsman as Prince Giglio.

I hope you do not imagine that there was any impropriety in the

Prince and Princess walking together in the palace garden, and because Giglio kissed Angelica's hand in a polite manner. In the first place they are cousins; next, the Queen is walking in the garden too (you cannot see her, for she happens to be behind that tree), and her Majesty always wished that Angelica and Giglio should marry: so did Giglio: so did Angelica sometimes, for she thought her cousin very

handsome, brave, and good-natured: but then you know she was so clever and knew so many things, and poor Giglio knew nothing, and had no conversation. When they looked at the stars, what did Giglio know of the heavenly bodies? Once, when on a sweet night in a balcony where they were standing, Angelica said, "There is the Bear." "Where?" says Giglio. "Don't be afraid, Angelica! if a dozen bears come, I will kill them rather than they shall hurt you." "Oh, you silly

creature!" says she: "you are very good, but you are not very wise."
When they looked at the flowers, Giglio was utterly unacquainted with
botany, and had never heard of Linnæus. When the butterflies passed
Giglio knew nothing about them, being as ignorant of entomology as I
am of algebra. So you see, Angelica, though she liked Giglio pretty

well, despised him on account of his ignorance. I think she probably
valued *her own learning* rather too much; but to think too well of
one's self is the fault of people of all ages and both sexes. Finally,
when nobody else was there, Angelica liked her cousin well enough.

King Valoroso was very delicate in health, and withal so fond of

good dinners (which were prepared for him by his French cook
Marmitonio), that it was supposed he could not live long.   Now the
idea of anything happening to the King struck the artful Prime
Minister and the designing old lady-in-waiting with terror.   For,
thought Glumboso and the Countess, "when Prince Giglio marries his
cousin and comes to the throne, what a pretty position we shall be in,
whom he dislikes, and who have always been unkind to him.   We shall
lose our places in a trice ; Gruffanuff will have to give up all the jewels,

laces, snuff-boxes, rings, and watches which belonged to the Queen,
Giglio's mother ; and Glumboso will be forced to refund two hundred
and seventeen thousand millions, nine hundred and eighty-seven
thousand, four hundred and thirty-nine pounds, thirteen shillings, and
sixpence halfpenny, money left to Prince Giglio by his poor dear father."
So the Lady of Honour and the Prime Minister hated Giglio because
they had done him a wrong ; and these unprincipled people invented a
hundred cruel stories about poor Giglio, in order to influence the King,

Queen, and Princess against him; how he was so ignorant that he could not spell the commonest words, and actually wrote Valoroso Valloroso, and spelt Angelica with two l's; how he drank a great deal too much wine at dinner, and was always idling in the stables with the grooms; how he owed ever so much money at the pastrycook's and the haberdasher's; how he used to go to sleep at church; how he was fond of playing cards with the pages.   So did the Queen like playing

cards; so did the King go to sleep at church, and eat and drink too much; and, if Giglio owed a trifle for tarts, who owed him two hundred and seventeen thousand millions, nine hundred and eighty-seven thousand, four hundred and thirty-nine pounds, thirteen shillings, and sixpence halfpenny, I should like to know? Detractors and tale-bearers (in my humble opinion) had much better look at *home*. All this backbiting and slandering had effect upon Princess Angelica, who began to look coldly on her cousin, then to laugh at him and scorn him for being so stupid, then to sneer at him for having vulgar associates; and at Court balls, dinners, and so forth, to treat him so unkindly that poor Giglio became quite ill, took to his bed, and sent for the doctor.

His Majesty King Valoroso, as we have seen, had his own reasons for disliking his nephew; and as for those innocent readers who ask why?—I beg (with the permission of their dear parents) to refer them to Shakespeare's pages, where they will read why King John disliked

Prince Arthur. With the Queen, his royal but weak-minded aunt, when Giglio was out of sight he was out of mind. While she had her whist and her evening-parties, she cared for little else.

I dare say *two villains,* who shall be nameless, wished Doctor Pildrafto, the Court Physician, had killed Giglio right out, but he only bled and physicked him so severely, that the Prince was kept to his room for several months, and grew as thin as a post.

Whilst he was lying sick in this way, there came to the Court of Paflagonia a famous painter, whose name was Tomaso Lorenzo, and who was Painter in Ordinary to the King of Crim Tartary, Paflagonia's neighbour. Tomaso Lorenzo painted all the Court, who were delighted with his works ; for even Countess Gruffanuff looked young and Glumboso good-humoured in his pictures. "He flatters very much," some people said. "Nay !" says Princess Angelica, "I am above flattery, and I think he did not make my picture handsome enough. I can't bear to hear a man of genius unjustly cried down, and I hope my dear papa will make Lorenzo a knight of his Order of the Cucumber."

The Princess Angelica, although the courtiers vowed her Royal Highness could draw so *beautifully* that the idea of her taking lessons was absurd, yet chose to have Lorenzo for a teacher, and it was wonderful, *as long as she painted in his studio,* what beautiful pictures she made ! Some of the performances were engraved for the Book of Beauty : others were sold for enormous sums at Charity Bazaars. She wrote the *signatures* under the drawings, no doubt, but I think I know who did the pictures—this artful painter, who had come with other designs on Angelica than merely to teach her to draw.

One day, Lorenzo showed the Princess a portrait of a young man in armour, with fair hair and the loveliest blue eyes, and an expression at once melancholy and interesting.

"Dear Signor Lorenzo, who is this ?" asked the Princess. "I never saw any one so handsome," says Countess Gruffanuff (the old humbug).

"That," said the painter, "that, madam, is the portrait of my august young master, his Royal Highness Bulbo, Crown Prince of Crim Tartary, Duke of Acroceraunia, Marquis of Poluphloisboio, and Knight Grand Cross of the Order of the Pumpkin. That is the Order of the Pumpkin glittering on his manly breast, and received by his Royal Highness from his august father, his Majesty King PADELLA I., for his gallantry at the battle of Rimbombamento, when he slew **with** his own princely hand the King of Ograria and two hundred and eleven giants of the two hundred and eighteen who formed the King's body-guard. The remainder were destroyed by the brave Crim Tartar army after an obstinate combat, in which the Crim Tartars suffered severely."

What a Prince! thought Angelica: so brave—so calm-looking—so young—what a hero!

"He is as accomplished as he is brave," continued the Court Painter. "He knows all languages perfectly: sings deliciously: plays every instrument: composes operas which have been acted a thousand nights running at the Imperial Theatre of Crim Tartary, and danced in a ballet there before the King and Queen ; in which he looked so beautiful, that his cousin, the lovely daughter of the King of Circassia, died for love of him."

"Why did he not marry the poor Princess ?" asked Angelica, with a sigh.

"Because they were *first cousins*, madam, and the clergy forbid these unions," said the Painter. "And, besides, the young Prince had given his royal heart *elsewhere*."

"And to whom?" asked her Royal Highness.

"I am not at liberty to mention the Princess's name," answered the Painter.

"But you may tell me the first letter of it," gasped out the Princess.

"That your Royal Highness is at liberty to guess," says Lorenzo.

"Does it begin with a Z?" asked Angelica.

The Painter said it wasn't a Z ; then she tried a Y ; then an X ; then a W, and went so backwards through almost the whole alphabet.

When she came to D, and it wasn't D, she grew very much excited ; when she came to C, and it wasn't C, she was still more nervous ; when she came to B, *and it wasn't B*, "O dearest Gruffanuff," she said, "lend me your smelling-bottle !" and, hiding her head in the Countess's shoulder, she faintly whispered, "Ah, Signor, can it be A?"

"It was A ; and though I may not, by my Royal Master's orders, tell your Royal Highness the Princess's name, whom he fondly, madly, devotedly, rapturously loves, I may show you her portrait," says the slyboots : and leading the Princess up to a gilt frame, he drew a curtain which was before it.

O goodness ! the frame contained A LOOKING-GLASS ! and Angelica saw her own face !

VII.

HOW GIGLIO AND ANGELICA HAD A QUARREL.

THE Court Painter of his Majesty the King of Crim Tartary returned to that monarch's dominions, carrying away a number of sketches which he had made in the Paflagonian capital (you know, of course, my dears, that the name of that capital is Blombodinga) ; but the most charming of all his pieces was a portrait of the Princess Angelica, which all the Crim Tartar nobles came to see. With this work the King was so delighted, that he decorated the Painter with his Order of the Pumpkin (sixth class), and the artist became Sir Tomaso Lorenzo, K.P., thenceforth.

King Valoroso also sent Sir Tomaso his Order of the Cucumber, besides a handsome order for money, for he painted the King, Queen, and principal nobility while at Blombodinga, and became all the fashion, to the perfect rage of all the artists in Paflagonia, where the King used to point to the portrait of Prince Bulbo, which Sir Tomaso had left behind him, and say, "Which among you can paint a picture like that?"

It hung in the royal parlour over the royal sideboard, and Princess Angelica could always look at it as she sat making the tea. Each day it seemed to grow handsomer and handsomer, and the Princess grew so fond of looking at it, that she would often spill the tea over the cloth, at which her father and mother would wink and wag their heads, and say to each other, "Aha! we see how things are going."

In the meanwhile poor Giglio lay upstairs very sick in his chamber, though he took all the doctor's horrible medicines like a good young lad ; as I hope *you* do, my dears, when you are ill and mamma sends for the medical man. And the only person who visited Giglio (besides his friend the captain of the guard, who was almost always busy or on parade), was little Betsinda the housemaid, who used to do his bedroom and sitting-room out, bring him his gruel, and warm his bed.

When the little housemaid came to him in the morning and evening, Prince Giglio used to say, "Betsinda, Betsinda, how is the Princess Angelica?"

And Betsinda used to answer, "The Princess is very well, thank you, my Lord." And Giglio would heave a sigh, and think, if Angelica were sick, I am sure *I* should not be very well.

Then Giglio would say, "Betsinda, has the Princess Angelica asked for me to-day?" And Betsinda would answer, "No, my Lord, not to-day;" or, "she was very busy practising the piano when I saw her;" or, "she was writing invitations for an evening-party, and did not speak to me :" or make some excuse or other, not strictly consonant with truth : for Betsinda was such a good-natured creature, that she strove to do everything to prevent annoyance to Prince Giglio, and even brought him up roast chicken and jellies from the kitchen (when the Doctor allowed them, and Giglio was getting better), saying, "that the Princess had made the jelly or the bread sauce with her own hands, on purpose for Giglio."

When Giglio heard this he took heart, and began to mend immediately; and gobbled up all the jelly, and picked the last bone of the chicken—drumsticks, merry-thought, sides'-bones, back, pope's nose, and all—thanking his dear Angelica : and he felt so much better the next day, that he dressed and went downstairs, where, whom should he meet but Angelica going into the drawing-room? All the covers were off the chairs, the chandeliers taken out of the bags, the damask curtains uncovered, the work and things carried away, and the handsomest albums on the tables. Angelica had her hair in papers : in a word, it was evident there was going to be a party.

"Heavens, Giglio!" cries Angelica : "*you* here in such a dress! What a figure you are!"

"Yes, dear Angelica, I am come downstairs, and feel so well to-day, thanks to the *fowl* and the *jelly*."

"What do I know about fowls and jellies, that you allude to them in that rude way?" says Angelica.

"Why, didn't—didn't you send them, Angelica dear?" says Giglio.

"I send them indeed! Angelica dear! No, Giglio dear," says she, mocking him, "*I* was engaged in getting the rooms ready for his Royal Highness the Prince of Crim Tartary, who is coming to pay my papa's Court a visit."

"The—Prince—of—Crim—Tartary!" Giglio said, aghast.

"Yes, the Prince of Crim Tartary," says Angelica, mocking him. "I daresay you never heard of such a country. What *did* you ever hear of? You don't know whether Crim Tartary is on the Red Sea or on the Black Sea, I daresay."

"Yes, I do, it's on the Red Sea," says Giglio, at which the Princess burst out laughing at him, and said, "O you ninny! You are so ignorant, you are really not fit for society ! You know nothing but about horses and dogs, and are only fit to dine in a mess-room with my Royal father's heaviest dragoons. Don't look so surprised at me, sir : go and put your best clothes on to receive the Prince, and let me get the drawing-room ready."

Giglio said, " O Angelica, Angelica, I didn't think this of you. *This* wasn't your language to me when you gave me this ring, and I gave you mine in the garden, and you gave me that k—"

But what k— was we never shall know, for Angelica, in a rage, cried, " Get out, you saucy, rude creature ! How dare you to remind me of your rudeness ? As for your little trumpery twopenny ring, there, sir, there ! " And she flung it out of the window.

" It was my mother's marriage-ring," cried Giglio.

" *I* don't care whose marriage-ring it was," cries Angelica. " Marry the person who picks it up if she's a woman ; you sha'n't marry *me*. And give me back *my* ring. I've no patience with people who boast about the things they give away ! *I* know who'll give me much finer things than you ever gave me. A beggarly ring indeed, not worth five shillings ! "

Now Angelica little knew that the ring which Giglio had given her was a fairy ring : if a man wore it, it made all the women in love with him ; if a woman, all the gentlemen. The Queen, Giglio's mother, quite an ordinary-looking person, was admired immensely whilst she wore this ring, and her husband was frantic when she was ill. But when she called her little Giglio to her, and put the ring on his finger, King Savio did not seem to care for his wife so much any more, but transferred all his love to little Giglio. So did everybody love him as long as he had the ring ; but when, as quite a child, he gave it to Angelica, people began to love and admire *her ;* and Giglio, as the saying is, played only second fiddle.

" Yes," says Angelica, going on in her foolish ungrateful way, " I know who'll give me much finer things than your beggarly little pearl nonsense."

" Very good, Miss ! You may take back your ring, too ! " says Giglio, his eyes flashing fire at her, and then, as if his eyes had been suddenly opened, he cried out, " Ha ! what does this mean ? Is *this* the woman I have been in love with all my life ? Have I been such a ninny as to throw away my regard upon *you ?* Why—actually—yes—you are a little crooked ! "

" O, you wretch ! " cries Angelica.

" And, upon my conscience, you—you squint a little."

"Eh!" cries Angelica.

"And your hair is red—and you are marked with the small-pox—and what? you have three false teeth—and one leg shorter than the other!"

"You brute, you brute, you!" Angelica screamed out : and as she seized the ring with one hand, she dealt Giglio one, two, three smacks on the face, and would have pulled the hair off his head had he not started laughing, and crying,

"O dear me, Angelica, don't pull out *my* hair, it hurts! You might remove a great deal of *your own*, as I perceive, without scissors or pulling at all. O, ho, ho! ha, ha, ha! he, he, he!"

And he nearly choked himself with laughing, and she with rage; when, with a low bow, and dressed in his Court habit, Count Gambabella, the first lord-in-waiting, entered and said, "Royal Highnesses! Their Majesties expect you in the Pink Throne-room, where they await the arrival of the Prince of CRIM TARTARY."

VIII.

HOW GRUFFANUFF PICKED THE FAIRY RING UP, AND PRINCE BULBO CAME TO COURT.

PRINCE BULBO'S arrival had set all the Court in a flutter : everybody was ordered to put his or her best clothes on : the footmen had their gala liveries ; the Lord Chancellor his new wig ; the
Guards their last new tunics ; and Countess Gruffanuff you may be
sure was glad of an opportunity of decorating *her* old person with her

finest things. She was walking through the court of the Palace on
her way to wait upon their Majesties, when she spied something glittering on the pavement, and bade the boy in buttons who was holding

up her train, to go and pick up the article shining yonder. He was
an ugly little wretch, in some of the late groom-porter's old clothes
cut down, and much too tight for him; and yet, when he had taken up

HIS R.H. THE PRINCE OF CRIM TARTARY.

the ring (as it turned out to be), and was carrying it to his mistress, she thought he looked like a little Cupid. He gave the ring to her; it was a trumpery little thing enough, but too small for any of her old knuckles, so she put it into her pocket.

"O, mum!" says the boy, looking at her, "how—how beyoutiful you do look, mum, to-day, mum!"

"And you, too, Jacky," she was going to say; but, looking down at him—no, he was no longer good-looking at all—but only the carrotty-haired little Jacky of the morning. However, praise is welcome from the ugliest of men or boys, and Gruffanuff, bidding the boy hold up her train, walked on in high good-humour. The guards saluted her with peculiar respect. Captain Hedzoff, in the ante-room, said, "My dear madam, you look like an angel to-day." And so, bowing and smirking, Gruffanuff went in and took her place behind her Royal Master and Mistress, who were in the throne-room, awaiting the Prince of Crim Tartary. Princess Angelica sat at their feet, and behind the King's chair stood Prince Giglio, looking very savage.

The Prince of Crim Tartary made his appearance, attended by Baron Sleibootz, his chamberlain, and followed by a black page, carrying the most beautiful crown you ever saw! He was dressed in his travelling costume, and his hair was a little in disorder. "I have ridden three hundred miles since breakfast," said he, "so eager was I to behold the Prin—the Court and august family of Paflagonia, and I could not wait one minute before appearing in your Majesties' presences."

Giglio, from behind the throne, burst out into a roar of contemptuous laughter; but all the Royal party, in fact, were so flurried, that they did not hear this little outbreak. "Your R. H. is welcome in any dress," says the King. "Glumboso, a chair for his Royal Highness."

"Any dress his Royal Highness wears *is* a Court dress," says Princess Angelica, smiling graciously.

"Ah! but you should see my other clothes," said the Prince. "I should have had them on, but that stupid carrier has not brought them. Who's that laughing?"

It was Gigiio laughing. "I was laughing," he said, "because you said just now that you were in such a hurry to see the Princess, that you could not wait to change your dress; and now you say you come in those clothes because you have no others."

"And who are you?" says Prince Bulbo, very fiercely.

"My father was King of this country, and I am his only son, Prince!" replies Giglio, with equal haughtiness.

"Ha!" said the King and Glumboso, looking very flurried; but the former, collecting himself, said, "Dear Prince Bulbo, I forgot to introduce to your Royal Highness my dear nephew, his Royal Highness Prince Giglio! Know each other! Embrace each other! Giglio, give his Royal Highness your hand!" And Giglio, giving his hand, squeezed poor Bulbo's, until the tears ran out of his eyes. Glumboso now brought a chair for the Royal visitor, and placed it on the platform on which the King, Queen, and Prince were seated; but the chair was on the edge of the platform, and as Bulbo sat down, it toppled over, and he with it, rolling over and over, and bellowing like a bull. Giglio roared still louder at this disaster, but it was with laughter; so did all the Court when Prince Bulbo got up; for though when he entered the room he appeared not very ridiculous, as he stood up from his fall for a moment, he looked so exceedingly plain and foolish, that nobody could help laughing at him. When he had entered the room, he was observed to carry a rose in his hand, which fell out of it as he tumbled.

"My rose! my rose!" cried Bulbo; and his chamberlain dashed forwards and picked it up, and gave it to the Prince, who put it in his waistcoat. Then people wondered why they had laughed; there was nothing particularly ridiculous in him. He was rather short, rather stout, rather red-haired, but, in fine, for a Prince, not so bad.

So they sat and talked, the royal personages together, the Crim Tartar officers with those of Paflagonia—Giglio very comfortable with Gruffanuff behind the throne. He looked at her with such tender eyes, that her heart was all in a flutter. "Oh, dear Prince," she said, "how could you speak so haughtily in presence of their Majesties? I protest I thought I should have fainted."

"I should have caught you in my arms," said Giglio, looking raptures.

"Why were you so cruel to Prince Bulbo, dear Prince?" says Gruff.

"Because I hate him," says Gil.

"You are jealous of him, and still love poor Angelica," cries Gruffanuff, putting her handkerchief to her eyes.

"I did, but I love her no more!" Giglio cried. "I despise her! Were she heiress to twenty thousand thrones, I would despise her and scorn her. But why speak of thrones? I have lost mine. I am too weak to recover it—I am alone, and have no friend.'

"Oh, say not so, dear Prince!" says Gruffanuff.

"Besides," says he, "I am so happy here *behind the throne*, that I would not change my place, no, not for the throne of the world!"

"What are you two people chattering about there?" says the Queen, who was rather good-natured, though not over-burthened with wisdom. "It s time to dress for dinner. Giglio, show Prince Bulbo

to his room. Prince, if your clothes have not come, we shall be very happy to see you as you are." But when Prince Bulbo got to his bedroom, his luggage was there and unpacked; and the hairdresser coming in, cut and curled him entirely to his own satisfaction; and when the dinner-bell rang, the royal company had not to wait above five-and-twenty minutes until Bulbo appeared, during which time the King, who could not bear to wait, grew as sulky as possible. As for

Giglio, he never left Madam Gruffanuff all this time, but stood with her in the embrasure of a window, paying her compliments. At length the Groom of the Chambers announced his Royal Highness the

Prince of Crim Tartary! and the noble company went into the royal dining-room. It was quite a small party; only the King and Queen, the Princess, whom Bulbo took out, the two Princes, Countess Gruffanuff, Glumboso the Prime Minister, and Prince Bulbo's chamberlain.

You may be sure they had a very good dinner—let every boy or girl think of what he or she likes best, and fancy it on the table.*

The Princess talked incessantly all dinner time to the Prince of Crimea, who ate an immense deal too much, and never took his eyes off his plate, except when Giglio, who was carving a goose, sent a quantity of stuffing and onion sauce into one of them. Giglio only burst out a laughing as the Crimean Prince wiped his shirt-front and face with his scented pocket-handkerchief. He did not make Prince Bulbo any apology. When the Prince looked at him, Giglio would not look that way. When Prince Bulbo said, " Prince Giglio, may I have the honour of taking a glass of wine with you ?" Giglio *wouldn't* answer. All his talk and his eyes were for Countess Gruffanuff, who you may be sure was pleased with Giglio's attentions—the vain old creature ! When he was not complimenting her, he was making fun of Prince Bulbo, so loud that Gruffanuff was always tapping him with her fan, and saying,

" O you satirical Prince ! O fie, the Prince will hear ! "

" Well, I don't mind," says Giglio, louder still.

The King and Queen luckily did not hear; for her Majesty was a little deaf, and the King thought so much about his own dinner, and, besides, made such a dreadful noise, hob-gobbling in eating it, that he heard nothing else. After dinner, his Majesty and the Queen went to sleep in their arm-chairs.

This was the time when Giglio began his tricks with Prince Bulbo, plying that young gentleman with port, sherry, madeira, champagne, marsala, cherry brandy and pale ale, of all of which Master Bulbo drank without stint. But in plying his guest, Giglio was obliged to drink himself, and, I am sorry to say, took more than was good for him, so that the young men were very noisy, rude, and foolish when they joined the ladies after dinner; and dearly did they pay for that imprudence, as now, my darlings, you shall hear !

Bulbo went and sat by the piano, where Angelica was playing and singing, and he sang out of tune, and he upset the coffee when the footman brought it, and he laughed out of place, and talked absurdly, and fell asleep and snored horridly. Booh, the nasty pig ! But as he lay there stretched on the pink satin sofa, Angelica still persisted in thinking him the most beautiful of human beings. No doubt the magic rose which Bulbo wore, caused this infatuation on Angelica's

---

* Here a very pretty game may be played by all the children saying what they like best for dinner.

part; but is she the first young woman who has thought a silly fellow charming?

Giglio must go and sit by Gruffanuff, whose old face he too every moment began to find more lovely. He paid the most outrageous compliments to her:—There never was such a darling. Older than he was?—Fiddle-de-dee! He would marry her—he would have nothing but her!

To marry the heir to the throne! Here was a chance! The artful hussy actually got a sheet of paper, and wrote upon it, "This is to give notice that I, Giglio, only son of Savio, King of Paflagonia, hereby promise to marry the charming and virtuous Barbara Griselda Countess Gruffanuff, and widow of the late Jenkins Gruffanuff, Esq."

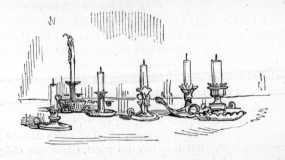

"What is it you are writing? you charming Gruffy!" says Giglio, who was lolling on the sofa, by the writing-table.

"Only an order for you to sign, dear Prince, for giving coals and blankets to the poor, this cold weather. Look! the King and Queen are both asleep, and your Royal Highness's order will do."

So Giglio, who was very good-natured, as Gruffy well knew, signed the order immediately; and, when she had it in her pocket, you may fancy what airs she gave herself. She was ready to flounce out of the room before the Queen herself, as now she was the wife of the *rightful* King of Paflagonia! She would not speak to Glumboso, whom she thought a brute, for depriving her *dear husband* of the crown! An when candles came, and she had helped to undress the Queen and Princess, she went into her own room, and actually practised, on a sheet of paper, " Griselda Paflagonia," " Barbara Regina," " Griselda Barbara, Paf. Reg.," and I don't know what signatures besides, against the day when she should be Queen, forsooth !

IX.

HOW BETSINDA GOT THE WARMING-PAN.

LITTLE Betsinda came in to put Gruffanuff's hair in papers; and
the Countess was so pleased, that, for a wonder, she compli
mented Betsinda. " Betsinda ! " she said, " you dressed my hair very
nicely to-day; I promised you a little present. Here are five sh— no
here is a pretty little ring, that I picked—that I have had som
time." And she gave Betsinda the ring she had picked up in th
court.   It fitted Betsinda exactly.

" It's like the ring the Princess used to wear," says the maid.

" No such thing," says Gruffanuff, " I have had it this ever so long. There—tuck me up quite comfortable; and now, as it's a very cold night (the snow was beating in at the window) you may go and warm dear Prince Giglio's bed, like a good girl, and then you may unrip my green silk, and then you can just do me up a little cap for the morning, and then you can mend that hole in my silk stocking, and then you can go to bed, Betsinda. Mind, I shall want my cup of tea at five o'clock in the morning."

" I suppose I had best warm both the young gentlemen's beds, ma'am," says Betsinda.

Gruffanuff, for reply, said, " Hau-au-ho !—Grau-haw-hoo !—Hong-hrho ! " In fact, she was snoring sound asleep.

Her room, you know, is next to the King and Queen, and the Princess is next to them. So pretty Betsinda went away for the coals to the kitchen, and filled the royal warming-pan.

Now, she was a very kind, merry, civil, pretty girl; but there must have been something very captivating about her this evening, for all the women in the servants'-hall began to scold and abuse her. The housekeeper said she was a pert, stuck-up thing : the upper-housemaid asked, how dare she wear such ringlets and ribbons, it was quite improper ! The cook (for there was a woman-cook as well as a man-cook) said to the kitchen-maid that *she* never could see anything in that creetur : but as for the men, every one of them, Coachman, John, Buttons the page, and Monsieur, the Prince of Crim Tartary's valet, started up, and said—

" My eyes ! "
" O mussey ! "
" O jemmany ! " } " What a pretty girl Betsinda is ! "
" O ciel ! "

" Hands off ; none of your impertinence, you vulgar, low people ! " says Betsinda, walking off with her pan of coals. She heard the young gentlemen playing at billiards as she went upstairs : first to Prince Giglio's bed, which she warmed, and then to Prince Bulbo's room.

He came in just as she had done ; and as soon as he saw her, " O ! O ! O ! O ! O ! O ! what a beyou—oo—ootiful creature you are ! You angel—you peri—you rosebud, let me be thy bulbul—thy Bulbo, too ! Fly to the desert, fly with me ! I never saw a young gazelle to glad me with its dark blue eye that had eyes like thine. Thou nymph of beauty, take, take this young heart. A truer never did itself sustain

within a soldier's waistcoat. Be mine! Be mine! Be Princess of
Crim Tartary! My Royal Father will approve our union: and, as
for that little carrotty-haired Angelica, I do not care a fig for her any
more."

"Go away, your Royal Highness, and go to bed, please," said
Betsinda, with the warming-pan.

But Bulbo said, "No, never, till thou swearest to be mine, thou

lovely, blushing, chambermaid divine! Here, at thy feet, the Royal
Bulbo lies, the trembling captive of Betsinda's eyes."

And he went on, making himself so *absurd and ridiculous*, that
Betsinda, who was full of fun, gave him a touch with the warming-
pan, which, I promise you, made him cry "O-o-o-o!" in a very different manner.

Prince Bulbo made such a noise that Prince Giglio, who heard him
from the next room, came in to see what was the matter. As soon as

THE RIVALS.

he saw what was taking place, Giglio, in a fury, rushed on Bulbo, kicked him in the rudest manner up to the ceiling, and went on kicking him till his hair was quite out of curl.

Poor Betsinda did not know whether to laugh or to cry; the kicking certainly must hurt the Prince, but then he looked so droll! When Giglio had done knocking him up and down to the ground, and whilst he went into a corner rubbing himself, what do you think Giglio does? He goes down on his own knees to Betsinda, takes her hand, begs her to accept his heart, and offers to marry her that moment. Fancy Betsinda's condition, who had been in love with the Prince ever since she first saw him in the palace garden, when she was quite a little child.

"Oh, divine Betsinda!" says the Prince, "how have I lived fifteen years in thy company without seeing thy perfections? What woman in all Europe, Asia, Africa, and America, nay, in Australia, only it is not yet discovered, can presume to be thy equal? Angelica? Pish! Gruffanuff? Phoo! The Queen? Ha, ha! Thou art my Queen. Thou art the real Angelica, because thou art really angelic."

"Oh, Prince! I am but a poor chambermaid," says Betsinda, looking, however, very much pleased.

"Didst thou not tend me in my sickness, when all forsook me?" continues Giglio. "Did not thy gentle hand smooth my pillow, and bring me jelly and roast chicken?"

"Yes, dear Prince, I did," says Betsinda, "and I sewed your Royal Highness's shirt-buttons on too, if you please, your Royal Highness," cries this artless maiden.

When poor Prince Bulbo, who was now madly in love with Betsinda, heard this declaration, when he saw the unmistakable glances which she flung upon Giglio, Bulbo began to cry bitterly, and tore quantities of hair out of his head, till it all covered the room like so much tow.

Betsinda had left the warming-pan on the floor while the Princes were going on with their conversation, and as they began now to quarrel and be very fierce with one another, she thought proper to run away.

"You great big blubbering booby, tearing your hair in the corner there; of course you will give me satisfaction for insulting Betsinda. *You* dare to kneel down at Princess Giglio's knees and kiss her hand!"

"She's not Princess Giglio!" roars out Bulbo. "She shall be Princess Bulbo, no other shall be Princess Bulbo."

" You are engaged to my cousin ! " bellows out Giglio.

" I hate your cousin," says Bulbo.

" You shall give me satisfaction for insulting her ! " cries Giglio in a fury.

" I'll have your life."

" I'll run you through."

" I'll cut your throat."

" I'll blow your brains out."

" I'll knock your head off."

" I'll send a friend to you in the morning."

" I'll send a bullet into you in the afternoon."

" We'll meet again," says Giglio, shaking his fist in Bulbo's face ; and seizing up the warming-pan, he kissed it, because, forsooth, Betsinda had carried it, and rushed downstairs. What should he see on the landing but his Majesty talking to Betsinda, whom he called by all sorts of fond names. His Majesty had heard a row in the building, so he stated, and smelling something burning, had come out to see what the matter was.

" It's the young gentlemen smoking, perhaps, sir," says Betsinda.

" Charming chambermaid," says the King (like all the rest of them), " never mind the young men ! Turn thy eyes on a middle-aged autocrat, who has been considered not ill-looking in his time."

" Oh, sir ! what will her Majesty say ? " cries Betsinda.

" Her Majesty ! " laughs the monarch. " Her Majesty be hanged. Am I not Autocrat of Paflagonia? Have I not blocks, ropes, axes, hangmen—ha? Runs not a river by my palace wall? Have I not sacks to sew up wives withal? Say but the word, that thou wilt be mine own,—your mistress straightway in a sack is sewn, and thou the sharer of my heart and throne."

When Giglio heard these atrocious sentiments, he forgot the respect usually paid to Royalty, lifted up the warming-pan, and knocked down the King as flat as a pancake ; after which, master Giglio took to his heels and ran away, and Betsinda went off screaming, and the Queen, Gruffanuff, and the Princess, all came out of their rooms. Fancy their feelings on beholding their husband, father, sovereign in this posture !

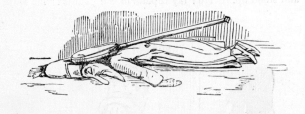

X.

HOW KING VALOROSO WAS IN A DREADFUL PASSION.

A S soon as the coals began to burn him, the King came to himself
and stood up. "Ho! my captain of the guards!" his Majesty

exclaimed, stamping his royal feet with rage. O piteous spectacle! the
King's nose was bent quite crooked by the blow of Prince Giglio! His

Majesty ground his teeth with rage. " Hedzoff," he said, taking a
death-warrant out of his dressing-gown pocket, " Hedzoff, good
Hedzoff, seize upon the Prince. Thou'lt find him in his chamber two
pair up. But now he dared, with sacrilegious hand, to strike the sacred
nightcap of a king—Hedzoff, and floor me with a warming-pan ! Away,
no more demur, the villain dies ! see it be done, or else,—h'm !—ha !
—h'm ! mind thine own eyes !" and followed by the ladies, and

lifting up the tails of his dressing-gown, the King entered his own
apartment.

Captain Hedzoff was very much affected, having a sincere love for
Giglio. " Poor, poor Giglio !" he said, the tears rolling over his manly
face, and dripping down his moustachios ; "my noble young Prince, is
it my hand must lead thee to death ? "

"Lead him to fiddlestick, Hedzoff," said a female voice. It was

Gruffanuff, who had come out in her dressing-gown when she heard the noise. "The King said you were to hang the Prince. Well, hang the Prince."

"I don't understand you," says Hedzoff, who was not a very clever man.

"You Gaby ! he didn't say *which* Prince," says Gruffanuff.

"No ; he didn't say which, certainly," said Hedzoff.

"Well then, take Bulbo, and hang *him !*"

When Captain Hedzoff heard this, he began to dance about for joy. "Obedience is a soldier's honour," says he. "Prince Bulbo's head will do capitally," and he went to arrest the Prince the very first thing next morning.

He knocked at the door. "Who's there ?" says Bulbo. "Captain Hedzoff ? step in, pray, my good Captain ; I'm delighted to see you ; I have been expecting you."

"Have you ?" says Hedzoff.

"Sleibootz, my Chamberlain, will act for me," says the Prince.

"I beg your Royal Highness's pardon, but you will have to act for yourself, and it's a pity to wake Baron Sleibootz."

The Prince Bulbo still seemed to take the matter very coolly. "Of course, Captain," says he, "you are come about that affair with Prince Giglio ?"

"Precisely," says Hedzoff, "that affair of Prince Giglio."

"Is it to be pistols, or swords, Captain ?" asks Bulbo. "I'm a pretty good hand with both, and I'll do for Prince Giglio as sure as my name is my Royal Highness Prince Bulbo."

"There's some mistake, my Lord," says the Captain. "The business is done with *axes* among us."

"Axes ? That's sharp work," says Bulbo. "Call my Chamberlain, he'll be my second, and in ten minutes, I flatter myself, you'll see Master Giglio's head off his impertinent shoulders. I'm hungry for his blood. Hoo-oo, aw! " and he looked as savage as an ogre.

"I beg your pardon, sir, but by this warrant I am to take you prisoner, and hand you over to—to the executioner."

"Pooh, pooh, my good man !—Stop, I say,—ho !—hulloa !" was all that this luckless Prince was enabled to say, for Hedzoff's guards seizing him, tied a handkerchief over his mouth and face, and carried him to the place of execution.

The King, who happened to be talking to Glumboso, saw him pass and took a pinch of snuff, and said, "So much for Giglio. Now let's go to breakfast."

The Captain of the Guard handed over his prisoner to the Sheriff, with the fatal order,

"At sight cut off the bearer's head.
"Valoroso XXIV."

"It's a mistake," says Bulbo, who did not seem to understand the business in the least.

"Poo—poo—pooh," says the Sheriff. "Fetch Jack Ketch instantly. Jack Ketch!"

And poor Bulbo was led to the scaffold, where an executioner with a block and a tremendous axe was always ready in case he should be wanted.

But we must now revert to Giglio and Betsinda.

XI.

WHAT GRUFFANUFF DID TO GIGLIO AND BETSINDA.

GRUFFANUFF, who had seen what had happened with the King, and knew that Giglio must come to grief, got up very early the next morning, and went to devise some plans for rescuing her darling husband, as the silly old thing insisted on calling him. She found him walking up and down the garden, thinking of a rhyme for Betsinda (*tinder* and *winda* were all he could find), and indeed having forgotten all about the past evening, except that Betsinda was the most lovely of beings.

"Well, dear Giglio," says Gruff.

"Well, dear Gruffy," says Giglio, only *he* was quite satirical.

"I have been thinking, darling, what you must do in this scrape. You must fly the country for a while."

"What scrape?—fly the country? Never without her I love, Countess," says Giglio.

"No, she will accompany you, dear Prince," she says, in her most coaxing accents. "First, we must get the jewels belonging to our royal parents, and those of her and his present Majesty. Here is the key, duck; they are all yours, you know, by right, for you are the rightful King of Paflagonia, and your wife will be the rightful Queen."

"Will she?" says Giglio.

"Yes; and having got the jewels, go to Glumboso's apartment, where, under his bed, you will find sacks containing money to the amount of £217,000,987,439 13s. 6½d., all belonging to you, for he took it out of your royal father's room on the day of his death. With this we will fly."

"*We* will fly?" says Giglio.

"Yes, you and your bride—your affianced love—your Gruffy!" says the Countess, with a languishing leer.

"*You* my bride!" says Giglio.   "You, you hideous old woman!"

"Oh, you—you wretch! didn't you give me this paper promising marriage?" cries Gruff.

"Get away, you old goose!   I love Betsinda, and Betsinda only!" And in a fit of terror he ran from her as quickly as he could.

"He! he! he!" shrieks out Gruff; "a promise is a promise if there are laws in Paflagonia!   And as for that monster, that wretch, that fiend, that ugly little vixen—as for that upstart, that ingrate, that beast Betsinda, Master Giglio will have no little difficulty in discovering her whereabouts.   He may look very long before finding *her*, I warrant.   He little knows that Miss Betsinda is——"

Is—what? Now, you shall hear. Poor Betsinda got up at five on a winter's morning to bring her cruel mistress her tea; and instead of finding her in a good humour, found Gruffy as cross as two sticks. The Countess boxed Betsinda's ears half-a-dozen times whilst she was dressing; but as poor little Betsinda was used to this kind of treatment, she did not feel any special alarm. "And now," says she, "when her Majesty rings her bell twice, I'll trouble you, miss, to attend."

So when the Queen's bell rang twice, Betsinda came to her Majesty and made a pretty little curtsey. The Queen, the Princess, and Gruffanuff were all three in the room. As soon as they saw her they began.

"You wretch!" says the Queen.

"You little vulgar thing!" says the Princess.

"You beast!" says Gruffanuff.

"Get out of my sight!" says the Queen.

"Go away with you, do!" says the Princess.

"Quit the premises!" says Gruffanuff.

Alas! and woe is me! very lamentable events had occurred to Betsinda that morning, and all in consequence of that fatal warming-pan business of the previous night. The King had offered to marry her; of course her Majesty the Queen was jealous: Bulbo had fallen in love with her; of course Angelica was furious: Giglio was in love with her, and oh, what a fury Gruffy was in!

"Take off that $\left\{ \begin{array}{l} \text{cap} \\ \text{petticoat} \\ \text{gown} \end{array} \right\}$ I gave you," they said, all at once,

and began tearing the clothes off poor Betsinda.

"How dare you flirt with $\left\{ \begin{array}{l} \text{the King?"} \\ \text{Prince Bulbo?"} \\ \text{Prince Giglio?"} \end{array} \right\}$ cried the Queen, the Princess, and Countess.

"Give her the rags she wore when she came into the house, and turn her out of it!" cries the Queen.

"Mind she does not go with *my* shoes on, which I lent her so kindly," says the Princess; and indeed the Princess's shoes were a great deal too big for Betsinda.

"Come with me, you filthy hussy!" and taking up the Queen's poker, the cruel Gruffanuff drove Betsinda into her room.

The Countess went to the glass box in which she had kept Betsinda's old cloak and shoe this ever so long, and said, "Take those rags, you little beggar creature, and strip off everything belonging to honest people, and go about your business ; " and she actually tore off the poor little delicate thing's back almost all her things, and told her to be off out of the house.

Poor Betsinda huddled the cloak round her back, on which were

embroidered the letters PRIN . . . . ROSAL . . . and then came a great rent.

As for the shoe, what was she to do with one poor little tootsey sandal ? the string was still to it, so she hung it round her neck.

"Won't you give me a pair of shoes to go out in the snow, mum, if you please, mum?" cried the poor child.

"No, you wicked beast!" says Gruffanuff, driving her along with the poker—driving her down the cold stairs—driving her through the cold hall—flinging her out into the cold street, so that the knocker itself shed tears to see her!

But a kind fairy made the soft snow warm for her little feet, and she wrapped herself up in the ermine of her mantle, and was gone!

"And now let us think about breakfast," says the greedy Queen.

"What dress shall I put on, mamma? the pink or the pea-green?" says Angelica. "Which do you think the dear Prince will like best?"

"Mrs. V.!" sings out the King from his dressing-room, "let us have sausages for breakfast! Remember we have Prince Bulbo staying with us!"

And they all went to get ready.

Nine o'clock came, and they were all in the breakfast-room, and no Prince Bulbo as yet. The urn was hissing and humming: the muffins were smoking—such a heap of muffins! the eggs were done, there was a pot of raspberry jam, and coffee, and a beautiful chicken and tongue on the side-table. Marmitonio the cook brought in the sausages. Oh, how nice they smelt!

"Where is Bulbo?" said the King. "John, where is his Royal Highness?"

John said he had a took up his Roilighnessesses shaving-water, and his clothes and things, and he wasn't in his room, which he sposed his Royliness was just stepped hout.

"Stepped out before breakfast in the snow! Impossible!" says the King, sticking his fork into a sausage. "My dear, take one. Angelica, won't you have a saveloy?" The Princess took one, being very fond of them; and at this moment Glumboso entered with Captain Hedzoff, both looking very much disturbed.

"I am afraid your Majesty—" cries Glumboso.

"No business before breakfast, Glum!" says the King. "Breakfast first, business next. Mrs. V., some more sugar!"

"Sire, I am afraid if we wait till after breakfast it will be too late," says Glumboso. "He—he—he'll be hanged at half-past nine."

"Don't talk about hanging and spoil my breakfast, you unkind vulgar man you," cries the Princess. "John, some mustard. Pray who is to be hanged?"

"Sire, it is the Prince," whispers Glumboso to the King.

"Talk about business after breakfast, I tell you!" says his Majesty, quite sulky.

"We shall have a war, Sire, depend on it," says the Minister. "His father, King Padella . . . . "

"His father, King *who?*" says the King. "King Padella is not Giglio's father. My brother, King Savio, was Giglio's father."

"It's Prince Bulbo they are hanging, Sire, not Prince Giglio," says the Prime Minister.

"You told me to hang the Prince, and I took the ugly one," says Hedzoff. "I didn't, of course, think your Majesty intended to murder your own flesh and blood!"

The King for all reply flung the plate of sausages at Hedzoff's head. The Princess cried out "Hee-karee-karee!" and fell down in a fainting fit.

"Turn the cock of the urn upon her Royal Highness," said the King, and the boiling water gradually revived her. His Majesty looked at his watch, compared it by the clock in the parlour, and by that of the church in the square opposite; then he wound it up; then he looked at it again. "The great question is," says he, "am I fast or am I slow? If I'm slow, we may as well go on with breakfast. If I'm fast, why, there is just the possibility of saving Prince Bulbo. It's a doosid awkward mistake, and upon my word, Hedzoff, I have the greatest mind to have you hanged too."

"Sire, I did but my duty; a soldier has but his orders. I didn't expect after forty-seven years of faithful service that my sovereign would think of putting me to a felon's death!"

"A hundred thousand plagues upon you! Can't you see that while you are talking my Bulbo is being hanged?" screamed the Princess.

"By Jove! she's always right, that girl, and I'm so absent," says the King, looking at his watch again. "Ha! Hark, there go the drums! What a doosid awkward thing though!"

"O papa, you goose! Write the reprieve, and let me run with it," cries the Princess—and she got a sheet of paper, and pen and ink, and laid them before the King.

"Confound it! where are my spectacles?" the Monarch exclaimed. "Angelica! Go up into my bedroom, look under my pillow, not your mamma's; there you'll see my keys. Bring them down to me, and— Well, well! what impetuous things these girls are!" Angelica was gone, and had run up panting to the bedroom, and found the keys, and was back again before the King had finished a muffin. "Now, love," says he, "you must go all the way back for my desk, in which m

ANGELICA ARRIVES JUST IN TIME.

spectacles are. If you *would* but have heard me out . . . Be hanged to her! There she is off again. Angelica! ANGELICA!" When his Majesty called in his *loud* voice, she knew she must obey, and came back.

"My dear, when you go out of a room, how often have I told you, *shut the door.* That's a darling. That's all." At last the keys and the desk and the spectacles were got, and the King mended his pen, and signed his name to a reprieve, and Angelica ran with it as swift as the wind. "You'd better stay, my love, and finish the muffins. There's no use going. Be sure it's too late. Hand me over that raspberry jam, please," said the Monarch. "Bong! Bawong! There goes the half-hour. I knew it was."

Angelica ran, and ran, and ran, and ran. She ran up Fore Street, and down High Street, and through the Market-place, and down to the left, and over the bridge, and up the blind alley, and back again, and round by the Castle, and so along by the Haberdasher's on the right, opposite the lamp-post, and round the square, and she came— she came to the *Execution place*, where she saw Bulbo laying his head on the block ! ! ! The executioner raised his axe, but at that moment the Princess came panting up and cried "Reprieve!" "Reprieve!" screamed the Princess. "Reprieve!" shouted all the people. Up the scaffold stairs she sprang, with the agility of a lighter of lamps ; and flinging herself in Bulbo's arms, regardless of all ceremony, she cried out, "O my Prince! my lord! my love! my Bulbo! Thine Angelica has been in time to save thy precious existence, sweet rose-bud; to prevent thy being nipped in thy young bloom! Had aught befallen thee, Angelica too had died, and welcomed death that joined her to her Bulbo."

"H'm! there's no accounting for tastes," said Bulbo, looking so very much puzzled and uncomfortable, that the Princess, in tones of tenderest strain, asked the cause of his disquiet.

"I tell you what it is, Angelica," said he : "since I came here yester-day, there has been such a row, and disturbance, and quarrelling, and fighting, and chopping of heads off, and the deuce to pay, that I am inclined to go back to Crim Tartary."

"But with me as thy bride, my Bulbo! Though wherever thou art is Crim Tartary to me, my bold, my beautiful, my Bulbo!"

"Well, well, I suppose we must be married," says Bulbo. "Doctor, you came to read the Funeral Service—read the Marriage Service, will you? What must be, must. That will satisfy Angelica, and then, in the name of peace and quietness, do let us go back to breakfast."

Bulbo had carried a rose in his mouth all the time of the dismal ceremony. It was a fairy rose, and he was told by his mother that he ought never to part with it. So he had kept it between his teeth, even when he laid his poor head upon the block, hoping vaguely that some chance would turn up in his favour. As he began to speak to Angelica, he forgot about the rose, and of course it dropped out of his mouth. The romantic Princess instantly stooped and seized it. "Sweet rose!" she exclaimed, "that bloomed upon my Bulbo's lip, never, never will I part from thee!" and she placed it in her bosom. And you know Bulbo *couldn't* ask her to give the rose back again. And they went to breakfast; and as they walked, it appeared to Bulbo that Angelica became more exquisitely lovely every moment.

He was frantic until they were married; and now, strange to say, it was Angelica who didn't care about him! He knelt down, he kissed her hand, he prayed and begged; he cried with admiration; while she for her part said she really thought they might wait; it seemed to her he was not handsome any more—no, not at all, quite the reverse; and not clever, no, very stupid; and not well bred, like Giglio; no, on the contrary, dreadfully vul——

What, I cannot say, for King Valoroso roared out "*Pooh*, stuff!" in a terrible voice. "We will have no more of this shilly-shallying! Call the Archbishop, and let the Prince and Princess be married offhand!"

So, married they were, and I am sure for my part I trust they will be happy.

XI'.

HOW BETSINDA FLED, AND WHAT BECAME OF HER.

BETSINDA wandered on and on, till she passed through the town gates, and so on the great Crim Tartary road, the very way on which Giglio too was going. "Ah!" thought she, as the diligence passed her, of which the conductor was blowing a delightful tune on his horn, "how I should like to be on that coach!" But the coach and the jingling horses were very soon gone. She little knew who was in it, though very likely she was thinking of him all the time.

Then came an empty cart, returning from market ; and the driver being a kind man, and seeing such a very pretty girl trudging along the road with bare feet, most good-naturedly gave her a seat. He said he lived on the confines of the forest, where his old father was a woodman, and, if she liked, he would take her so far on her road. All roads

were the same to little Betsinda, so she very thankfully took this one.

And the carter put a cloth round her bare feet, and gave her some bread and cold bacon, and was very kind to her. For all that she was very cold and melancholy. When after travelling on and on, evening came, and all the black pines were bending with snow, and there, at last, was the comfortable light beaming in the woodman's windows ;

and so they arrived, and went into his cottage. He was an old man, and had a number of children, who were just at supper, with nice hot bread-and-milk, when their elder brother arrived with the cart. And they jumped and clapped their hands; for they were good children; and he had brought them toys from the town. And when they saw the pretty stranger, they ran to her, and brought her to the fire, and rubbed her poor little feet, and brought her bread-and-milk.

"Look, father!" they said to the old woodman, "look at this poor girl, and see what pretty cold feet she has. They are as white as our milk! And look and see what an odd cloak she has, just like the bit of velvet that hangs up in our cupboard, and which you found that day the little cubs were killed by King Padella, in the forest! And look,

why, bless us all! she has got round her neck just such another little shoe as that you brought home, and have shown us so often—a little blue velvet shoe!"

"What," said the old woodman, "what is all this about a shoe and a cloak?"

And Betsinda explained that she had been left, when quite a little child, at the town with this cloak and this shoe. And the persons who had taken care of her had—had been angry with her, for no fault, she hoped, of her own. And they had sent her away with her old clothes —and here, in fact, she was. She remembered having been in a forest —and perhaps it was a dream—it was so very odd and strange—having lived in a cave with lions there; and, before that, having lived in a very, very fine house, as fine as the King's, in the town.

When the woodman heard this, he was so astonished, it was quite curious to see how astonished he was. He went to his cupboard, and took out of a stocking a five-shilling piece of King Cavolfiore, and vowed it was exactly like the young woman. And then he produced the shoe and the piece of velvet which he had kept so long, and compared them with the things which Betsinda wore. In Betsinda's little shoe was written, " Hopkins, maker to the Royal Family ; " so in the other shoe was written, " Hopkins, maker to the Royal Family." In the inside of Betsinda's piece of cloak was embroidered, " PRIN ROSAL ;" in the other piece of cloak was embroidered " CESS BA. No. 246." So that when put together you read, " PRINCESS ROSALBA. No. 246."

On seeing this, the dear old woodman fell down on his knee, saying : " O my princess, O my gracious royal lady, O my rightful Queen of Crim Tartary,—I hail thee—I acknowledge thee—I do thee homage ! " And in token of his fealty, he rubbed his venerable nose three times on the ground, and put the Princess's foot on his head.

"Why," said she, "my good woodman, you must be a nobleman of my royal father's Court ! " For in her lowly retreat, and under the name of Betsinda, HER MAJESTY ROSALBA, Queen of Crim Tartary, had read of the customs of all foreign courts and nations.

" Marry, indeed am I, my gracious liege—the poor Lord Spinachi, once—the humble woodman these fifteen years syne. Ever since the tyrant Padella (may ruin overtake the treacherous knave !) dismissed me from my post of First Lord."

"First Lord of the Toothpick and Joint Keeper of the Snuff-box ? I mind me ! Thou heldest these posts under our royal Sire. They are restored to thee, Lord Spinachi ! I make thee knight of the second class of our Order of the Pumpkin (the first class being reserved for crowned heads alone). Rise, Marquis of Spinachi ! " And with indescribable majesty, the Queen, who had no sword handy, waved the pewter spoon with which she had been taking her bread-and-milk, over the bald head of the old nobleman, whose tears absolutely made a puddle on the ground, and whose dear children went to bed that night Lords and Ladies Bartolomeo, Ubaldo, Catarina, and Ottavia degli Spinachi !

The acquaintance HER MAJESTY showed with the history, and *noble families* of her empire, was wonderful. " The House of Broccoli should remain faithful to us," she said ; " they were ever welcome at our Court. Have the Articiocchi, as was their wont, turned to the Rising Sun ? The family of Sauerkraut must sure be with us—they were ever welcome in the halls of King Cavolfiore." And so she went on enumerating quite a list of the nobility and gentry of Crim Tartary, so admirably had her Majesty profited by her studies while in exile.

The old Marquis of Spinachi said he could answer for them all; that the whole country groaned under Padella's tyranny, and longed to return to its rightful sovereign; and late as it was, he sent his children, who knew the forest well, to summon this nobleman and that; and when his eldest son, who had been rubbing the horse down and giving him his supper, came into the house for his own, the Marquis

told him to put his boots on, and a saddle on the mare, and ride hither and thither to such and such people.

When the young man heard who his companion in the cart had been, he too knelt down and put her royal foot on his head; he too bedewed the ground with his tears; he was frantically in love with her, as everybody now was who saw her: so were the young Lords Bartolomeo and Ubaldo, who punched each other's little heads out of jealousy: and so, when they came from east and west at the summons of the Marquis degli Spinachi, were the Crim Tartar Lords who still remained faithful to the House of Cavolfiore. They were such very old gentlemen for the most part, that her Majesty never suspected their absurd passion, and went among them quite unaware of the havoc her beauty was causing, until an old blind Lord who had joined her party, told her what the truth was ; after which, for fear of making the people too much in love with her, she always wore a veil. She went about privately, from one nobleman's castle to another : and they visited among themselves again, and had meetings, and composed proclamations and counter-proclamations, and distributed all the best places of the kingdom amongst one another, and selected who of the opposition party should be executed when the Queen came to her own. And so in about a year they were ready to move.

The party of Fidelity was in truth composed of very feeble old fogies for the most part ; they went about the country waving their old swords and flags, and calling " God save the Queen ! " and King Padella happening to be absent upon an invasion, they had their own way for a little, and to be sure the people were very enthusiastic whenever they saw the Queen ; otherwise the vulgar took matters very quietly, for they said, as far as they could recollect, they were pretty well as much taxed in Cavolfiore's time, as now in Padella's.

XIII.

HOW QUEEN ROSALBA CAME TO THE CASTLE OF THE BOLD COUNT HOGGINARMO.

HER MAJESTY, having indeed nothing else to give, made all her followers Knights of the Pumpkin, and Marquises, Earls, and Baronets; and they had a little court for her, and made her a little crown of gilt paper, and a robe of cotton velvet; and they quarrelled about the places to be given away in her court, and about rank and precedence and dignities;—you can't think how they quarrelled! The poor Queen was very tired of her honours before she had had them a month, and I dare say sighed sometimes even to be a lady's-maid again. But we must all do our duty in our respective stations, so the Queen resigned herself to perform hers.

We have said how it happened that none of the Usurper's troops came out to oppose this Army of Fidelity: it pottered along as nimbly as the gout of the principal commanders allowed: it consisted of twice as many officers as soldiers: and at length passed near the estates of one of the most powerful noblemen of the country, who had not declared for the Queen, but of whom her party had hopes, as he was always quarrelling with King Padella.

When they came close to his park gates, this nobleman sent to say he would wait upon her Majesty: he was a most powerful warrior, and his name was Count Hogginarmo, whose helmet it took two strong negroes to carry. He knelt down before her and said, "Madam and liege lady! it becomes the great nobles of the Crimean realm to show every outward sign of respect to the wearer of the Crown, whoever that may be. We testify to our own nobility in acknowledging yours. The bold Hogginarmo bends the knee to the first of the aristocracy of his country."

Rosalba said, "The bold Count of Hogginarmo was uncommonly kind." But she felt afraid of him, even while he was kneeling, and his

eyes scowled at her from between his whiskers, which grew up to them.

"The first Count of the Empire, madam," he went on, "salutes the Sovereign. The Prince addresses himself to the not more noble lady !

Madam, my hand is free, and I offer it, and my heart and my sword to your service! My three wives lie buried in my ancestral vaults. The third perished but a year since; and this heart pines for a consort! Deign to be mine, and I swear to bring to your bridal table the head of King Padella, the eyes and nose of his son Prince Bulbo, the right hand and ears of the usurping Sovereign of Paflagonia, which country shall thenceforth be an appanage to your—to *our* Crown! Say yes; Hogginarmo is not accustomed to be denied. Indeed I cannot contemplate the possibility of a refusal; for frightful will be the result; dreadful the murders; furious the devastations; horrible the tyranny; tremendous the tortures, misery, taxation, which the people of this realm will endure, if Hogginarmo's wrath be aroused! I see consent in your Majesty's lovely eyes—their glances fill my soul with rapture!"

"O, sir!" Rosalba said, withdrawing her hand in great fright. "Your Lordship is exceedingly kind; but I am sorry to tell you that I have a prior attachment to a young gentleman by the name of—Prince —Giglio—and never—never can marry any one but him."

Who can describe Hogginarmo's wrath at this remark? Rising up from the ground, he ground his teeth so that fire flashed out of his mouth, from which at the same time issued remarks and language, so *loud, violent, and improper,* that this pen shall never repeat them! "R-r-r-r-r—Rejected! Fiends and perdition! The bold Hogginarmo rejected! All the world shall hear of my rage; and you, madam, you above all shall rue it!" And kicking the two negroes before him, he rushed away, his whiskers streaming in the wind.

Her Majesty's Privy Council was in a dreadful panic when they saw Hogginarmo issue from the royal presence in such a towering rage, making footballs of the poor negroes—a panic which the events justified. They marched off from Hogginarmo's park very crestfallen; and in another half-hour they were met by that rapacious chieftain with a few of his followers, who cut, slashed, charged, whacked, banged, and pommelled amongst them, took the Queen prisoner, and drove the Army of Fidelity to I don't know where.

Poor Queen! Hogginarmo, her conqueror, would not condescend to see her. "Get a horse-van!" he said to his grooms, "clap the hussy into it, and send her, with my compliments, to his Majesty King Padella."

Along with his lovely prisoner, Hogginarmo sent a letter full of servile compliments and loathsome flatteries to King Padella, for whose life, and that of his royal family, the *hypocritical humbug* pretended to offer the most fulsome prayers. And Hogginarmo promised speedily to pay his humble homage at his august master's throne, of which he begged leave to be counted the most loyal and constant defender. Such a *wary* old *bird* as King Padella was not to be caught by Master Hogginarmo's *chaff,* and we shall hear presently how the tyrant treated his upstart vassal. No, no ; depend on't, two such rogues do not trust one another.

So this poor Queen was laid in the straw like Margery Daw, and driven along in the dark ever so many miles to the Court, where King Padella had now arrived, having vanquished all his enemies, murdered most of them, and brought some of the richest into captivity with him for the purpose of torturing them and finding out where they had hidden their money.

Rosalba heard their shrieks and groans in the dungeon in which she was thrust ; a most awful black hole, full of bats, rats, mice, toads, frogs, mosquitoes, bugs, fleas, serpents, and every kind of horror. No light was let into it, otherwise the gaolers might have seen her and

fallen in love with her, as an owl that lived up in the roof of the tower did, and a cat, you know, who can see in the dark, and having set its green eyes on Rosalba, never could be got to go back to the turnkey's wife to whom it belonged. And the toads in the dungeon came and kissed her feet, and the vipers wound round her neck and arms, and never hurt her, so charming was this poor Princess in the midst of her misfortunes.

At last, after she had been kept in this place *ever so long*, the door of the dungeon opened, and the terrible KING PADELLA came in.

But what he said and did must be reserved for another chapter, as we must now go back to Prince Giglio.

XIV.

WHAT BECAME OF GIGLIO.

THE idea of marrying such an old creature as Gruffanuff, frightened Prince Giglio so, that he ran up to his room, packed his trunks, fetched in a couple of porters, and was off to the diligence office in a twinkling.

It was well that he was so quick in his operations, did not dawdle over his luggage, and took the early coach, for as soon as the mistake about Prince Bulbo was found out, that cruel Glumboso sent up a couple of policemen to Prince Giglio's room, with orders that he should be carried to Newgate, and his head taken off before twelve o'clock. But the coach was out of the Paflagonian dominions before two o'clock; and I daresay the express that was sent after Prince Giglio did not ride very quick, for many people in Paflagonia had a regard for Giglio, as the son of their old sovereign; a Prince who, with all his weaknesses, was very much better than his brother, the usurping, lazy, careless, passionate, tyrannical, reigning monarch. That Prince busied himself with the balls, fêtes, masquerades, hunting-parties, and so forth, which he thought proper to give on occasion of his daughter's marriage to Prince Bulbo; and let us trust was not sorry in his own heart that his brother's son had escaped the scaffold.

It was very cold weather, and the snow was on the ground, and Giglio, who gave his name as simple Mr. Giles, was very glad to get a comfortable place on the coupé of the diligence, where he sat with the conductor and another gentleman. At the first stage from Blombodinga, as they stopped to change horses, there came up to the diligence a very ordinary, vulgar-looking woman, with a bag under her arm, who asked for a place. All the inside places were taken, and the

young woman was informed that if she wished to travel, she must go
upon the roof ; and the passenger inside with Giglio (a rude person, I
should think), put his head out of the window, and said, " Nice
weather for travelling outside ! I wish you a pleasant journey, my

dear." The poor woman coughed very much, and Giglio pitied her.
" I will give up my place to her," says he, " rather than she should
travel in the cold air with that horrid cough." On which the vulgar
traveller said, " *You'd* keep her warm, I am sure, if it's a *muff* she
wants." On which Giglio pulled his nose, boxed his ears, hit him in

the eye, and gave this vulgar person a warning never to call him *muff*
again.

Then he sprang up gaily on to the roof of the diligence, and made
himself very comfortable in the straw.   The vulgar traveller got down
at the next station, and Giglio took his place again, and talked to
the person next to him.   She appeared to be a most agreeable, well-
informed, and entertaining female.   They travelled together till night,
and she gave Giglio all sorts of things out of the bag which she carried, and which indeed seemed to contain the most wonderful collec-
tion of articles.   He was thirsty—out there came a pint bottle of Bass's
pale ale, and a silver mug !   Hungry—she took out a cold fowl, some

slices of ham, bread, salt, and a most delicious piece of cold plum-
pudding, and a little glass of brandy afterwards.

As they travelled, this plain-looking, queer woman talked to Giglio
on a variety of subjects, in which the poor Prince showed his ignorance
as much as she did her capacity.   He owned, with many blushes, how
ignorant he was ; on which the lady said, " My dear Gigl—my good
Mr. Giles, you are a young man, and have plenty of time before you.
You have nothing to do but to improve yourself.   Who knows but
that you may find use for your knowledge some day ?   When—when
you may be wanted at home, as some people may be."

" Good heavens, madam ! " says he, " do you know me ? "

" I know a number of funny things," says the lady.   " I have been at some people's christenings, and turned away from other folks' doors. I have seen some people spoilt by good fortune, and others, as I hope, improved by hardship. I advise you to stay at the town where the coach stops for the night. Stay there and study, and remember your old friend to whom you were kind."

"And who is my old friend?" asked Giglio.

"When you want anything," says the lady, "look in this bag, which I leave to you as a present, and be grateful to—"

"To whom, madam?" says he.

"To the Fairy Blackstick," says the lady, flying out of the window. And when Giglio asked the conductor if he knew where the lady was?

"What lady?" says the man; "there has been no lady in this coach, except the old woman, who got out at the last stage." And Giglio thought he had been dreaming. But there was the bag which Blackstick had given him lying on his lap; and when he came to the town he took it in his hand and went into the inn.

They gave him a very bad bed-room, and Giglio, when he woke in the morning, fancying himself in the Royal Palace at home, called, "John, Charles, Thomas! My chocolate—my dressing-gown—my slippers;" but nobody came. There was no bell, so he went and bawled out for the waiter on the top of the stairs.

The landlady came up, looking—looking like this—

"What are you a hollaring and a bellaring for here, young man? says she.

"There's no warm water—no servants: my boots are not even cleaned."

"He, he! Clean 'em yourself," says the landlady. "You young students give yourselves pretty airs. I never heard such impudence."

"I'll quit the house this instant," says Giglio.

"The sooner the better, young man. Pay your bill and be off. All my rooms is wanted for gentlefolks, and not for such as you."

"You may well keep the Bear Inn," said Giglio. "You should have yourself painted as the sign."

The landlady of the Bear went away *growling*. And Giglio returned to his room, where the first thing he saw was the fairy bag lying on the table, which seemed to give a little hop as he came in.

"I hope it has some breakfast in it," says Giglio, "for I have only a very little money left."

But on opening the bag, what do you think was there? A blacking-brush and a pot of Warren's jet, and on the pot was written,

> "Poor young men their boots must black :
> Use me and cork me and put me back."

So Giglio laughed and blacked his boots, and put back the brush and the bottle into the bag.

When he had done dressing himself, the bag gave another little hop, and he went to it and took out—

1. A tablecloth and a napkin.
2. A sugar-basin full of the best loaf sugar.
4, 6, 8, 10. Two forks, two teaspoons, two knives, and a pair of sugar-tongs, and a butter-knife, all marked G.
11, 12, 13. A tea-cup, saucer, and slop-basin.
14. A jug full of delicious cream.
15. A canister with black tea and green.
16. A large tea-urn and boiling water.
17. A saucepan, containing three eggs nicely done.
18. A quarter of a pound of best Epping butter.
19. A brown loaf.

And if he hadn't enough now for a good breakfast, I should like to know who ever had one?

Giglio, having had his breakfast, popped all the things back into the bag, and went out looking for lodgings. I forgot to say that this celebrated university town was called Bosforo.

He took a modest lodging opposite the Schools, paid his bill at the inn, and went to his apartment with his trunk, carpet-bag, and not forgetting, we may be sure, his *other* bag.

When he opened his trunk, which the day before he had filled with

his best clothes, he found it contained only books.   And in the first of them which he opened there was written—

> "Clothes for the back, books for the head ;
> Read, and remember them when they are read."

And in his bag, when Giglio looked in it, he found a student's cap and gown, a writing-book full of paper, an inkstand, pens, and a Johnson's dictionary, which was very useful to him, as his spelling had been sadly neglected.

So he sat down and worked away, very, very hard for a whole year, during which "Mr. Giles" was quite an example to all the students in the University of Bosforo. He never got into any riots or disturbances. The Professors all spoke well of him, and the students liked him too; so that, when at examinations he took all the prizes, viz. :—

The Spelling Prize	The French Prize
The Writing Prize	The Arithmetic Prize
The History Prize	The Latin Prize
The Catechism Prize	The Good Conduct Prize,

all his fellow-students said, "Hurray! Hurray for Giles! Giles is the boy—the student's joy! Hurray for Giles!" And he brought quite a quantity of medals, crowns, books, and tokens of distinction home to his lodgings.

One day after the Examinations, as he was diverting himself at a coffee-house with two friends—(Did I tell you that in his bag, every Saturday night, he found just enough to pay his bills, with a guinea over, for pocket-money? Didn't I tell you? Well, he did, as sure as twice twenty makes forty-five)—he chanced to look in the *Bosforo Chronicle*, and read off quite easily (for he could spell, read, and write the longest words now) the following—

"ROMANTIC CIRCUMSTANCE.—One of the most extraordinary adventures that we have ever heard has set the neighbouring country of Crim Tartary in a state of great excitement.

"It will be remembered that when the present revered sovereign of Crim Tartary, his Majesty King *Padella*, took possession of the throne, after having vanquished, in the terrific battle of Blunderbusco, the late King *Cavolfiore*, that Prince's only child, the Princess Rosalba, was not found in the royal palace, of which King Padella took possession, and, it was said, had strayed into the forest (being abandoned by all her attendants), where she had been eaten up by those ferocious lions, the last pair of which were captured some time since, and brought to the Tower, after killing several hundred persons.

"His Majesty King Padella, who has the kindest heart in the

world, was grieved at the accident which had occurred to the harmless little Princess, for whom his Majesty's known benevolence would certainly have provided a fitting establishment. But her death seemed to be certain. The mangled remains of a cloak, and a little shoe, were found in the forest, during a hunting-party, in which the intrepid sovereign of Crim Tartary slew two of the lions' cubs with his own spear. And these interesting relics of an innocent little creature were carried home and kept by their finder, the Baron Spinachi, formerly an officer in Cavolfiore's household. The Baron was disgraced in consequence of his known legitimist opinions, and has lived for some time in the humble capacity of a woodcutter, in a forest on the outskirts of the Kingdom of Crim Tartary.

"Last Tuesday week Baron Spinachi and a number of gentlemen attached to the former dynasty, appeared in arms, crying, 'God save Rosalba, the First Queen of Crim Tartary!' and surrounding a lady whom report describes as *beautiful exceedingly.*' Her history *may* be authentic, *is* certainly most romantic.

"The personage calling herself Rosalba states that she was brought out of the forest, fifteen years since, by a lady in a car drawn by dragons (this account is certainly *improbable*), that she was left in the Palace Garden of Blombodinga, where her Royal Highness the Princess Angelica, now married to his Royal Highness Bulbo, Crown Prince of Crim Tartary, found the child, and, with *that elegant benevolence* which has always distinguished the heiress of the throne of Paflagonia, gave the little outcast a *shelter and a home!* Her parentage not being known, and her garb very humble, the foundling was educated in the Palace in a menial capacity, under the name of *Betsinda.*

"She did not give satisfaction, and was dismissed, carrying with her, certainly, part of a mantle and a shoe, which she had on when first found. According to her statement she quitted Blombodinga about a year ago, since which time she has been with the Spinachi family. On the very same morning the Prince Giglio, nephew to the King of Paflagonia, a young Prince whose character for *talent* and *order* were, to say truth, *none of the highest*, also quitted Blombodinga, and has not been since heard of!"

"What an extraordinary story!" said Smith and Jones, two young students, Giglio's especial friends.

"Ha! what is this?" Giglio went on, reading:

"SECOND EDITION, EXPRESS.—We hear that the troop under Baron Spinachi has been surrounded, and utterly routed, by General Count Hogginarmo, and the *soi-disant* Princess is sent a prisoner to the capital.

"UNIVERSITY NEWS.—Yesterday, at the Schools, the distinguished young student, Mr. Giles, read a Latin oration, and was complimented by the Chancellor of Bosforo, Doctor Prugnaro, with the highest University honour—the wooden spoon."

"Never mind that stuff," says *Giles*, greatly disturbed. "Come home with me, my friends. Gallant Smith! intrepid Jones! friends of my studies—partakers of my academic toils—I have that to tell shall astonish your honest minds."

"Go it, old boy!" cried the impetuous Smith.

"Talk away, my buck!" says Jones, a lively fellow.

With an air of indescribable dignity, Giglio checked their natural, but no more seemly, familiarity. "Jones, Smith, my good friends," said the PRINCE, "disguise is henceforth useless; I am no more the humble student Giles, I am the descendant of a royal line."

"*Atavis edite regibus*, I know, old co——," cried Jones. He was going to say old cock, but a flash from THE ROYAL EYE again awed him.

"Friends," continued the Prince, "I am that Giglio, I am in fact Paflagonia. Rise, Smith, and kneel not in the public street. Jones, thou true heart! My faithless uncle, when I was a baby, filched from me that brave crown my father left me, bred me, all young and careless of my rights, like unto hapless Hamlet, Prince of Denmark; and had I any thoughts about my wrongs, soothed me with promises of near redress. I should espouse his daughter, young Angelica; we two indeed should reign in Paflagonia. His words were false—false as Angelica's heart!—false as Angelica's hair, colour, front teeth! She looked with her skew eyes upon young Bulbo, Crim Tartary's stupid heir, and she preferred him. 'Twas then I turned my eyes upon Betsinda—Rosalba, as she now is. And I saw in her the blushing sum of all perfection; the pink of maiden modesty; the nymph that my fond heart had ever woo'd in dreams," &c., &c.

(I don't give this speech, which was very fine, but very long; and though Smith and Jones knew nothing about the circumstances, my dear reader does, so I go on.)

The Prince and his young friends hastened home to his apartment, highly excited by the intelligence, as no doubt by the *royal narrator's* admirable manner of recounting it ; and they ran up to his room where he had worked so hard at his books.

On his writing-table was his bag, grown so long that the Prince could not help remarking it. He went to it, opened it, and what do you think he found in it ?

A splendid long, gold-handled, red-velvet-scabbarded, cut-and-thrust sword, and on the sheath was embroidered " ROSALBA FOR EVER ! "

He drew out the sword, which flashed and illuminated the whole room, and called out " Rosalba for ever ! " Smith and Jones following him, but quite respectfully this time, and taking the time from his Royal Highness.

And now his trunk opened with a sudden pong, and out there came three ostrich feathers in a gold crown, surrounding a beautiful shining steel helmet, a cuirass, a pair of spurs, finally a complete suit of armour.

The books on Giglio's shelves were all gone. Where there had been some great dictionaries, Giglio's friends found two pairs of jack-boots labelled, " Lieutenant Smith," "——Jones, Esq.," which fitted them to a nicety. Besides, there were helmets, back- and breast-plates, swords, &c., just like in Mr. G. P. R. James's novels ; and that evening three cavaliers might have been seen issuing from the gates of Bosforo, in whom the porters, proctors, &c., never thought of recognizing the young Prince and his friends.

They got horses at a livery stable-keeper's, and never drew bridle until they reached the last town on the frontier before you come to Crim Tartary. Here, as their animals were tired, and the cavaliers hungry, they stopped and refreshed at an hostel. I could make a chapter of this if I were like some writers, but I like to cram my measure tight down, you see, and give you a great deal for your money, and in a word, they had some bread and cheese and ale upstairs on the balcony of the inn. As they were drinking, drums and trumpets sounded nearer and nearer, the market-place was filled with soldiers, and his Royal Highness looking forth, recognized the Paflagonian banners, and the Paflagonian national air which the bands were playing.

The troops all made for the tavern at once, and as they came up Giglio exclaimed, on beholding their leader, " Whom do I see ? Yes ! No ! It is, it is ! Phoo ! No, it can't be ! Yes ! it is my friend

TO ARMS.

PRINCE GIGLIO'S SPEECH TO THE ARMY.

21.

my gallant faithful veteran, Captain Hedzoff! Ho! Hedzoff! Knowest thou not thy Prince, thy Giglio? Good Corporal, methinks we once were friends. Ha, sergeant, an my memory serves me right, we have had many a bout at singlestick."

" I' faith, we have, a many, good my lord," says the sergeant.

" Tell me, what means this mighty armament," continued his Royal Highness from the balcony, " and whither march my Paflagonians ? "

Hedzoff's head fell. " My lord," he said, " we march as the allies of great Padella, Crim Tartary's monarch."

" Crim Tartary's usurper, gallant Hedzoff! Crim Tartary's grim tyrant, honest Hedzoff! " said the Prince, on the balcony, quite sarcastically.

" A soldier, Prince, must needs obey his orders : mine are to help his Majesty Padella. And also (though alack that I should say it !) to seize wherever I should light upon him—"

" First catch your hare ! ha, Hedzoff ! " exclaimed his royal Highness.

"—On the body of *Giglio*, whilome Prince of Paflagonia," Hedzoff went on, with indescribable emotion. " My Prince, give up your sword without ado. Look ! we are thirty thousand men to one ! "

" Give up my sword ! Giglio give up his sword ! " cried the Prince ; and stepping well forward on to the balcony, the royal youth, *without preparation*, delivered a speech so magnificent, that no report can do justice to it. It was all in blank verse (in which, from this time, he invariably spoke, as more becoming his majestic station). It lasted for three days and three nights, during which not a single person who heard him was tired, or remarked the difference between daylight and dark. The soldiers only cheering tremendously, when occasionally, once in nine hours, the Prince paused to suck an orange, which Jones took out of the bag. He explained, in terms which we say we shall not attempt to convey, the whole history of the previous transaction, and his determination not only not to give up his sword, but to assume his rightful crown ; and at the end of this extraordinary, this truly *gigantic* effort, Captain Hedzoff flung up his helmet, and cried, " Hurray ! Hurray ! Long live King Giglio ! "

Such were the consequences of having employed his time well at College !

When the excitement had ceased, beer was ordered out for the army, and their sovereign himself did not disdain a little ! And now

it was with some alarm that Captain Hedzoff told him his division
was only the advanced guard of the Paflagonian contingent, hastening
to King Padella's aid. The main force being a day's march in the rear
under his Royal Highness Prince Bulbo.

" We will wait here, good friend, to beat the Prince," his Majesty
said, " and *then* will make his royal Father wince."

XV.

WE RETURN TO ROSALBA.

KING PADELLA made very similar proposals to Rosalba to those which she had received from the various Princes who, as we have seen, had fallen in love with her. His Majesty was a widower, and offered to marry his fair captive that instant, but she declined his invitation in her usual polite gentle manner, stating that Prince Giglio was her love, and that any other union was out of the question. Having tried tears and supplications in vain, this violent-tempered monarch menaced her with threats and tortures ; but she declared she would rather suffer all these than accept the hand of her father's murderer, who left her finally, uttering the most awful imprecations, and bidding her prepare for death on the following morning.

All night long the King spent in advising how he should get rid of this obdurate young creature. Cutting off her head was much too easy a death for her ; hanging was so common in his Majesty's dominions that it no longer afforded him any sport : finally, he bethought himself of a pair of fierce lions which had lately been sent to him as presents, and he determined, with these ferocious brutes, to hunt poor Rosalba down. Adjoining his castle was an amphitheatre where the Prince indulged in bull-baiting, rat-hunting, and other ferocious sports. The two lions were kept in a cage under this place ; their roaring might be heard over the whole city, the inhabitants of which, I am sorry to say, thronged in numbers to see a poor young lady gobbled up by two wild beasts.

The King took his place in the royal box, having the officers of the Court around and the Count Hogginarmo by his side, upon whom his

Majesty was observed to look very fiercely; the fact is, royal spies had told the monarch of Hogginarmo's behaviour, his proposals to Rosalba, and his offer to fight for the crown. Black as thunder looked King Padella at this proud noble, as they sat in the front seats of the

theatre waiting to see the tragedy whereof poor Rosalba was to be the heroine.

At length that Princess was brought out in her night-gown, with all her beautiful hair falling down her back, and looking so pretty that even the beef-eaters and keepers of the wild animals wept plentifully

at seeing her. And she walked with her poor little feet (only luckily
the arena was covered with sawdust), and went and leaned up against
a great stone in the centre of the amphitheatre, round which the Court
and the people were seated in boxes, with bars before them, for fear of
the great, fierce, red-maned, black-throated, long-tailed, roaring, bellowing, rushing lions. And now the gates were opened, and with a
wurrawarrurawarar two great lean, hungry, roaring lions rushed out of
their den, where they had been kept for three weeks on nothing but a
little toast-and-water, and dashed straight up to the stone where poor

Rosalba was waiting. Commend her to your patron saints, all you kind
people, for she is in a dreadful state.

There was a hum and a buzz all through the circus, and the fierce
King Padella even felt a little compassion. But Count Hogginarmo,
seated by his Majesty, roared out, "Hurray! Now for it! Soo-soo-
soo!" that nobleman being uncommonly angry still at Rosalba's refusal
of him.

But O strange event! O remarkable circumstance! O extraordinary coincidence, which I am sure none of you could *by any possibility* have divined! When the lions came to Rosalba, instead of

devouring her with their great teeth, it was with kisses they gobbled her up! They licked her pretty feet, they nuzzled their noses in her lap, they moo'd, they seemed to say, "Dear, dear sister, don't you recollect your brothers in the forest?" And she put her pretty white arms round their tawny necks, and kissed them.

King Padella was immensely astonished. The Count Hogginarmo was extremely disgusted. "Pooh!" the Count cried. "Gammon!" exclaimed his lordship. "These lions are tame beasts come from Wombwell's or Astley's. It is a shame to put people off in this way. I believe they are little boys dressed up in door-mats. They are no lions at all."

"Ha!" said the King, "you dare to say 'gammon' to your sovereign, do you? These lions are no lions at all, aren't they? Ho, my beef-eaters! Ho! my body-guard! Take this Count Hogginarmo and fling him into the circus! Give him a sword and buckler, let him keep his armour on, and his weather-eye out, and fight these lions."

The haughty Hogginarmo laid down his opera-glass, and looked scowling round at the King and his attendants. "Touch me not, dogs!" he said, "or by St. Nicholas the Elder, I will gore you! Your Majesty thinks Hogginarmo is afraid? No, not of a hundred thousand lions! Follow me down into the circus, King Padella, and match thyself against one of yon brutes. Thou darest not. Let them both come on, then!"

And opening a grating of the box, he jumped lightly down into the circus.

Wurra wurra wurra wur-aw-aw-aw!!!
In about two minutes
The Count Hogginarmo was
GOBBLED UP
by
those lions,
bones, boots, and all,
and
There was an
End of him.

At this, the King said, "Serve him right, the rebellious ruffian! And now, as those lions won't eat that young woman——"

"Let her off!—let her off!" cried the crowd.

"NO!" roared the King. "Let the beef-eaters go down and chop her into small pieces. If the lions defend her, let the archers shoot them to death. That hussy shall die in tortures!"

"A-a-ah!" cried the crowd. "Shame! shame!"

"Who dares cry out shame?" cried the furious potentate (so little can tyrants command their passions). "Fling any scoundrel who says a word down among the lions!"

I warrant you there was a dead silence then, which was broken by a Pang arang pang pangkarangpang; and a Knight and a Herald rode in at the farther end of the circus. The Knight, in full armour, with his vizor up, and bearing a letter on the point of his lance.

"Ha!" exclaimed the King, "by my fay, 'tis Elephant and Castle, pursuivant of my brother of Paflagonia; and the Knight, an my memory serves me, is the gallant Captain Hedzoff! What news from Paflagonia, gallant Hedzoff? Elephant and Castle, beshrew me, thy trumpeting must have made thee thirsty. What will my trusty herald like to drink?"

"Bespeaking first safe conduct, from your Lordship," said Captain Hedzoff, "before we take a drink of anything, permit us to deliver our King's message."

"My lordship, ha!" said Crim Tartary, frowning terrifically. "That title soundeth strange in the anointed ears of a crowned King. Straightway speak out your message, Knight and Herald!"

Reining up his charger in a most elegant manner close under the King's balcony, Hedzoff turned to the herald, and bade him begin.

Elephant and Castle, dropping his trumpet over his shoulder, took a large sheet of paper out of his hat, and began to read:—

"*O Yes! O Yes! O Yes! Know all men by these presents, that we, Giglio, King of Paflagonia, Grand Duke of Cappadocia, Sovereign Prince of Turkey and the Sausage Islands, having assumed our rightful throne and title, long time falsely borne by our usurping Uncle, styling himself King of Paflagonia,—*"

"Ha!" growled Padella.

"*Hereby summon the false traitor, Padella, calling himself King of Crim Tartary,—*"

The King's curses were dreadful. "Go on, Elephant and Castle!" said the intrepid Hedzoff.

"*—To release from cowardly imprisonment his liege lady and rightful Sovereign, ROSALBA, Queen of Crim Tartary, and restore her to her royal throne: in default of which, I, Giglio, proclaim the said Padella, sneak, traitor, humbug, usurper, and coward. I challenge him to meet me, with fists or with pistols, with battle-axe or sword, with blunderbuss or singlestick, alone or at the head of his army, on foot or on horseback; and will prove my words upon his wicked ugly body!*"

"God save the King!" said Captain Hedzoff, executing a demivolte, two semilunes, and three caracols.

"Is that all?" said Padella, with the terrific calm of concentrated fury.

"That, sir, is all my royal master's message.   Here is his Majesty's letter in autograph, and here is his glove, and if any gentleman of Crim Tartary chooses to find fault with his Majesty's expressions, I, Kutasoff Hedzoff, Captain of the Guard, am very much at his service," and he waved his lance, and looked at the assembly all round.

"And what says my good brother of Paflagonia, my dear son's father-in-law, to this rubbish?" asked the King.

"The King's uncle hath been deprived of the crown he unjustly wore," said Hedzoff gravely. "He and his ex-minister, Glumboso, are now in prison waiting the sentence of my royal master.   After the battle of Bombardaro——"

"Of what?" asked the surprised Padella.

"Of Bombardaro, where my liege, his present Majesty, would have performed prodigies of valour, but that the whole of his uncle's army came over to our side, with the exception of Prince Bulbo."

"Ah! my boy, my boy, my Bulbo was no traitor!" cried Padella.

"Prince Bulbo, far from coming over to us, ran away, sir; but I caught him. The Prince is a prisoner in our army, and the most terrific tortures await him if a hair of the Princess Rosalba's head is injured."

"Do they?" exclaimed the furious Padella, who was now perfectly *livid* with rage. "Do they indeed? So much the worse for Bulbo. I've twenty sons as lovely each as Bulbo. Not one but is as fit to reig

as Bulbo. Whip, whack, flog, starve, rack, punish, torture Bulbo—
break all his bones—roast him or flay him alive—pull all his pretty
teeth out one by one ! but justly dear as Bulbo is to me,—Joy of my
eyes, fond treasure of my soul !—Ha, ha, ha, ha ! revenge is dearer still.
Ho ! torturers, rack-men, executioners—light up the fires and make
the pincers hot ! get lots of boiling lead !—Bring out ROSALBA ! "

XVI.

HOW HEDZOFF RODE BACK AGAIN TO KING GIGLIO.

CAPTAIN HEDZOFF rode away when King Padella uttered thi
cruel command, having done his duty in delivering the messag
with which his royal master had intrusted him. Of course he was ver
sorry for Rosalba, but what could he do?

So he returned to King Giglio's camp, and found the young monarc
in a disturbed state of mind, smoking cigars in the royal tent. H

POOR BULBO IS ORDERED FOR EXECUTION.

Majesty's agitation was not appeased by the news that was brought by his ambassador. "The brutal ruthless ruffian royal wretch!" Giglio exclaimed. "As England's poesy has well remarked, 'The man that lays his hand upon a woman, save in the way of kindness, is a villain.' Ha, Hedzoff?"

"That he is, your Majesty," said the attendant.

"And didst thou see her flung into the oil? and didn't the soothing oil—the emollient oil, refuse to boil, good Hedzoff—and to spoil the fairest lady ever eyes did look on?"

"Faith, good my liege, I had no heart to look and see a beauteous lady boiling down; I took your royal message to Padella, and bore his back to you. I told him you would hold Prince Bulbo answerable. He only said that he had twenty sons as good as Bulbo, and forthwith he bade the ruthless executioners proceed."

"O cruel father—O unhappy son!" cried the King. "Go, some of you, and bring Prince Bulbo hither."

Bulbo was brought in chains, looking very uncomfortable. Though a prisoner, he had been tolerably happy, perhaps because his mind was at rest, and all the fighting was over, and he was playing at marbles with his guards, when the King sent for him.

"O, my poor Bulbo," said his Majesty, with looks of infinite compassion, "hast thou heard the news?" (for you see Giglio wanted to break the thing gently to the Prince), "thy brutal father has condemned Rosalba—p-p-p-ut her to death, P-p-p-prince Bulbo!"

"What, killed Betsinda! Boo-hoo-hoo," cried out Bulbo. "Betsinda! pretty Betsinda! dear Betsinda! She was the dearest little girl in the world. I love her better twenty thousand times even than Angelica," and he went on expressing his grief in so hearty and unaffected a manner, that the King was quite touched by it, and said, shaking Bulbo's hand, that he wished he had known Bulbo sooner.

Bulbo, quite unconsciously, and meaning for the best, offered to come and sit with his Majesty, and smoke a cigar with him, and console him. The *royal kindness* supplied Bulbo with a cigar; he had not had one, he said, since he was taken prisoner.

And now think what must have been the feelings of the most *merciful of monarchs*, when he informed his prisoner that, in consequence of King Padella's *cruel and dastardly behaviour* to Rosalba, Prince Bulbo must instantly be executed! The noble Giglio could not restrain his tears, nor could the Grenadiers, nor the officers, nor could Bulbo himself, when the matter was explained to him, and he was brought to understand that his Majesty's promise, of course, was *above every* thing, and Bulbo must submit. So poor Bulbo was led out, Hedzoff trying to console him, by pointing out that if he had won the battle of Bombardaro, he might have hanged Prince Giglio. "Yes! But that is no comfort to me now!" said poor Bulbo; nor indeed was it, poor fellow!

He was told the business would be done the next morning at eight, and was taken back to his dungeon, where every attention was paid

to him. The gaoler's wife sent him tea, and the turnkey's daughter begged him to write his name in her album, where a many gentlemen had wrote it on like occasions! "Bother your album!" says Bulbo. The Undertaker came and measured him for the handsomest coffin which money could buy : even this didn't console Bulbo. The Cook brought him dishes which he once used to like; but he wouldn't touch them : he sat down and began writing an adieu to Angelica, as the clock kept always ticking, and the hands drawing nearer to next morning. The Barber came in at night, and offered to shave him for the next day. Prince Bulbo kicked him away, and went on writing a few words to Princess Angelica, as the clock kept always ticking, and the hands hopping nearer and nearer to next morning. He got up on the top of a hat-box, on the top of a chair, on the top of his bed, on the top of his table, and looked out to see whether he might escape as

the clock kept always ticking and the hands drawing nearer, and nearer, and nearer.

But looking out of the window was one thing, and jumping another: and the town clock struck seven. So he got into bed for a little sleep, but the gaoler came and woke him, and said, "Git up, your Royal Ighness, if you please, it's *ten minutes to eight*."

So poor Bulbo got up : he had gone to bed in his clothes (the lazy boy), and he shook himself, and said he didn't mind about dressing, or having any breakfast, thank you ; and he saw the soldiers who had come for him. "Lead on !" he said ; and they led the way, deeply affected ; and they came into the courtyard, and out into the square, and there was King Giglio come to take leave of him, and his Majesty most kindly shook hands with him, and the *gloomy procession* marched on :—when hark !

Haw—wurraw—wurraw—aworr !

A roar of wild beasts was heard. And who should come riding into the town, frightening away the boys, and even the beadle and policemen, but ROSALBA !

The fact is, that when Captain Hedzoff entered into the court of Snapdragon Castle, and was discoursing with King Padella, the Lions made a dash at the open gate, gobbled up the six beef-eaters in a jiffy

and away they went with Rosalba on the back of one of them, and
they carried her, turn and turn about, till they came to the city where
Prince Giglio's army was encamped.

When the KING heard of the QUEEN'S arrival, you may think how
he rushed out of his breakfast-room to hand her Majesty off her Lion!

The Lions were grown as fat as Pigs now, having eaten Hogginarmo
and all those beef-eaters, and were so tame, anybody might pat them.

While Giglio knelt (most gracefully) and helped the Princess,
Bulbo, for his part, rushed up and kissed the Lion. He flung his arms
round the forest monarch; he hugged him, and laughed and cried for

joy. "O you darling old beast, oh, how glad I am to see you, and the dear, dear Bets—that is, Rosalba."

"What, is it you? poor Bulbo!" said the Queen. "O, how glad *I* am to see you!" and she gave him her hand to kiss. King Giglio slapped him most kindly on the back, and said, "Bulbo, my boy, I am delighted, for your sake, that her Majesty has arrived."

"So am I," said Bulbo; "and *you know why*." Captain Hedzoff here came up. "Sire, it is half-past eight: shall we proceed with the execution?"

"Execution! what for?" asked Bulbo.

"An officer only knows his orders," replied Captain Hedzoff, showing his warrant, on which his Majesty King Giglio smilingly said, "Prince Bulbo was reprieved this time," and most graciously invited him to breakfast.

XVII.

HOW A TREMENDOUS BATTLE TOOK PLACE, AND WHO WON IT.

A S soon as King Padella heard, what we know already, that his
victim, the lovely Rosalba, had escaped him, his Majesty's fury
knew no bounds, and he pitched the Lord Chancellor, Lord Chamberlain, and every officer of the Crown whom he could set eyes on, into
the cauldron of boiling oil prepared for the Princess. Then he ordered
out his whole army, horse, foot, and artillery; and set forth at the
head of an innumerable host, and I should think twenty thousand
drummers, trumpeters, and fifers.

King Giglio's advanced guard, you may be sure, kept that monarch
acquainted with the enemy's dealings, and he was in no wise discon-
certed. He was much too polite to alarm the Princess, his lovely guest,
with any unnecessary rumours of battles impending; on the contrary,
he did everything to amuse and divert her; gave her a most elegant
breakfast, dinner, lunch, and got up a ball for her that evening, when
he danced with her every single dance.

Poor Bulbo was taken into favour again, and allowed to go quite
free now. He had new clothes given him, was called "My good cousin"
by his Majesty, and was treated with the greatest distinction by everybody. But it was easy to see he was very melancholy. The fact is,
the sight of Betsinda, who looked perfectly lovely in an elegant new
dress, set poor Bulbo frantic in love with her again. And he never
thought about Angelica, now Princess Bulbo, whom he had left at
home, and who, as we know, did not care much about him.

The King, dancing the twenty-fifth polka with Rosalba, remarked with wonder the ring she wore ; and then Rosalba told him how she had got it from Gruffanuff, who no doubt had picked it up when Angelica flung it away.

"Yes," says the Fairy Blackstick, who had come to see the young people, and who had very likely certain plans regarding them. "That ring I gave the Queen, Giglio's mother, who was not, saving your presence, a very wise woman ; it is enchanted, and whoever wears it looks beautiful in the eyes of the world. I made poor Prince Bulbo, when he was christened, the present of a rose which made him look handsome while he had it ; but he gave it to Angelica, who instantly looked beautiful again, whilst Bulbo relapsed into his natural plainness."

"Rosalba needs no ring, I'm sure," says Giglio, with a low bow. "She is beautiful enough, in my eyes, without any enchanted aid."

"O, sir !" said Rosalba.

"Take off the ring and try," said the King, and resolutely drew the ring off her finger. In *his* eyes she looked just as handsome as before !

The King was thinking of throwing the ring away, as it was so dangerous and made all the people so mad about Rosalba ; but being a Prince of great humour, and good-humour too, he cast eyes upon a poor youth who happened to be looking on very disconsolately, and said—

"Bulbo, my poor lad ! come and try on this ring. The Princess Rosalba makes it a present to you."

The magic properties of this ring were uncommonly strong, for no sooner had Bulbo put it on, but lo and behold, he appeared a personable, agreeable young Prince enough—with a fine complexion, fair hair, rather stout, and with bandy legs ; but these were encased in such a beautiful pair of yellow morocco boots that nobody remarked them. And Bulbo's spirits rose up almost immediately after he had looked in the glass, and he talked to their Majesties in the most lively, agreeable manner, and danced opposite the Queen with one of the prettiest maids of honour, and after looking at her Majesty, could not help saying—

"How very odd ! she is very pretty, but not so *extraordinarily* handsome."

"Oh no, by no means !" says the Maid of Honour.

"But what care I, dear sir," says the Queen, who overheard them, "if *you* think I am good-looking enough ? "

His Majesty's glance in reply to this affectionate speech was such that no painter could draw it.

And the Fairy Blackstick said, "Bless you, my darling children ! Now you are united and happy ; and now you see what I said from the first, that a little misfortune has done you both good. *You*, Giglio, had you been bred in prosperity, would scarcely have learned to read or write—you would have been idle and extravagant, and could not have been a good King, as you now will be. You, Rosalba, would have been so flattered, that your little head might have been turned like Angelica's, who thought herself too good for Giglio."

"As if anybody could be good enough for *him*," cried Rosalba.

"Oh, you, you darling !" says Giglio. And so she was ; and he was just holding out his arms in order to give her a hug before the whole company, when a messenger came rushing in, and said, "My lord, the enemy !"

"To arms !" cries Giglio.

"Oh, mercy !" says Rosalba, and fainted of course.

He snatched one kiss from her lips, and rushed *forth to the field* of battle !

The Fairy had provided King Giglio with a suit of armour, which was not only embroidered all over with jewels, and blinding to your eyes to look at, but was water-proof, gun-proof, and sword-proof ; so that in the midst of the very hottest battles his Majesty rode about as calmly as if he had been a British Grenadier at Alma. Were I engaged in fighting for my country, *I* should like such a suit of armour as Prince Giglio wore ; but, you know, he was a Prince of a fairy tale, and they always have these wonderful things.

Besides the fairy armour, the Prince had a fairy horse, which would gallop at any pace you please ; and a fairy sword, which would lengthen and run through a whole regiment of enemies at once. With such a weapon at command, I wonder, for my part, he thought of ordering his army out ; but forth they all came, in magnificent new uniforms ; Hedzoff and the Prince's two college friends each commanding a division, and his Majesty prancing in person at the head of them all.

Ah ! if I had the pen of a Sir Archibald Alison, my dear friends, would I not now entertain you with the account of a most tremendous shindy ? Should not fine blows be struck ? dreadful wounds be delivered ? arrows darken the air ? cannon balls crash through the battalions ? cavalry charge infantry ? infantry pitch into cavalry ?

bugles blow ; drums beat ; horses neigh ; fifes sing ; soldiers roar, swear, hurray ; officers shout out " Forward, my men !" " This way, lads !" " Give it 'em, boys !" " Fight for King Giglio, and the cause of right !" " King Padella for ever !" Would I not describe all this, I say, and in the very finest language too? But this humble pen does not possess the skill necessary for the description of combats. In a word, the overthrow of King Padella's army was so complete, that if they had been Russians you could not have wished them to be more utterly smashed and confounded.

As for that usurping monarch, having performed acts of valour much more considerable than could be expected of a royal ruffian and usurper, who had such a bad cause, and who was so cruel to women, —as for King Padella, I say, when his army ran away, the King ran away too, kicking his first general, Prince Punchikoff, from his saddle, and galloping away on the Prince's horse, having, indeed, had twenty-five or twenty-six of his own shot under him. Hedzoff coming up, and finding Punchikoff down, as you may imagine, very speedily disposed of *him*.

Meanwhile King Padella was scampering off as hard as his horse could lay legs to ground. Fast as he scampered, I promise you somebody else galloped faster ; and that individual, as no doubt you are aware, was the royal Giglio, who kept bawling out, " Stay, traitor ! Turn, miscreant, and defend thyself ! Stand, tyrant, coward, ruffian, royal wretch, till I cut thy ugly head from thy usurping shoulders! "

And, with his fairy sword, which elongated itself at will, his Majesty kept poking and prodding Padella in the back, until that wicked monarch roared with anguish.

When he was fairly brought to bay, Padella turned and dealt Prince Giglio a prodigious crack over the sconce with his battle-axe, a most enormous weapon, which had cut down I don't know how many regiments in the course of the afternoon. But, law bless you ! though the blow fell right down on his Majesty's helmet, it made no more impression than if Padella had struck him with a pat of butter : his battle-axe crumpled up in Padella's hand, and the Royal Giglio laughed for very scorn at the impotent efforts of that atrocious usurper.

At the ill success of his blow the Crim Tartar monarch was justly irritated.

" If," says he to Giglio, " you ride a fairy horse, and wear fairy armour, what on earth is the use of my hitting you ? I may as well give myself up a prisoner at once. Your Majesty won't, I suppose, be so mean as to strike a poor fellow who can't strike again ? "

THE TERRIFIC COMBAT BETWEEN KING GIGLIO AND KING PADELLA.

The justice of Padella's remark struck the magnanimous Giglio. "Do you yield yourself a prisoner, Padella?" says he.

"Of course I do," says Padella.

"Do you acknowledge Rosalba as your rightful Queen, and give up the crown and all your treasures to your rightful mistress?"

"If I must I must," says Padella, who was naturally very sulky.

By this time King Giglio's aides-de-camp had come up, whom his Majesty ordered to bind the prisoner. And they tied his hands behind him, and bound his legs tight under his horse, having set him with his face to the tail; and in this fashion he was led back to King Giglio's quarters, and thrust into the very dungeon where young Bulbo had been confined.

Padella (who was a very different person in the depth of his distress, to Padella, the proud wearer of the Crim Tartar crown,) now most affectionately and earnestly asked to see his son—his dear eldest boy—his darling Bulbo ; and that good-natured young man never once reproached his haughty parent for his unkind conduct the day before, when he would have left Bulbo to be shot without any pity, but came to see his father, and spoke to him through the grating of the door, beyond which he was not allowed to go ; and brought him some sandwiches from the grand supper which his Majesty was giving above stairs, in honour of the brilliant victory which had just been achieved.

"I cannot stay with you long, sir," says Bulbo, who was in his best ball dress, as he handed his father in the prog, "I am engaged to dance the next quadrille with her Majesty Queen Rosalba, and I hear the fiddles playing at this very moment."

So Bulbo went back to the ball-room, and the wretched Padella ate his solitary supper in silence and tears.

All was now joy in King Giglio's circle. Dancing, feasting, fun, illuminations, and jollifications of all sorts ensued. The people through whose villages they passed were ordered to illuminate their cottages at night, and scatter flowers on the roads during the day. They were requested, and I promise you they did not like to refuse, to serve the troops liberally with eatables and wine ; besides, the army was enriched by the immense quantity of plunder which was found in King Padella's camp, and taken from his soldiers ; who (after they had given up everything) were allowed to fraternise with the conquerors ; and the united forces marched back by easy stages towards King Giglio's capital, his royal banner and that of Queen Rosalba being carried in front of the troops. Hedzoff was made a Duke and a Field-Marshal. Smith and Jones were promoted to be Earls ; the Crim Tartar Order of the Pumpkin and the Paflagonian decoration of the Cucumber were freely distributed by their Majesties to the army. Queen Rosalba wore the Paflagonian Ribbon of the Cucumber across her riding habit, whilst King Giglio never appeared without the grand Cordon of the Pumpkin. How the people cheered them as they rode along side by side ! They were pronounced to be the handsomest couple ever seen : that was a matter of course ; but they really *were* very handsome, and, had they been otherwise, would have looked so, they were so happy ! Their Majesties were never separated during the whole day, but breakfasted, dined, and supped together always, and rode side by side, interchanging elegant compliments, and indulging in the most delightful conversation. At night, her Majesty's ladies of honour (who had all rallied round her the day after King Padella's defeat) came and conducted her to the apartments prepared for her; whilst King Giglio, surrounded by his gentlemen, withdrew to his own Royal quarters. It was agreed they should be married as soon as they reached the capital, and orders were despatched to the Archbishop of Blombodinga, to hold himself in readiness to perform the interesting ceremony. Duke Hedzoff carried

the message, and gave instructions to have the Royal Castle splendidly refurnished and painted afresh. The Duke seized Glumboso the Ex-Prime Minister, and made him refund that considerable sum of money which the old scoundrel had secreted out of the late King's treasure. He also clapped Valoroso into prison (who, by the way, had been dethroned for some considerable period past), and when the Ex-Monarch weakly remonstrated, Hedzoff said, "A soldier, sir, knows but his duty; my orders are to lock you up along with the Ex-King Padella, whom I have brought hither a prisoner under guard." So these two Ex-Royal personages were sent for a year to the House of Correction, and thereafter were obliged to become monks of the severest Order of Flagellants, in which state, by fasting, by vigils, by flogging (which they administered to one another, humbly but resolutely), no doubt they exhibited a repentance for their past misdeeds, usurpations, and private and public crimes.

As for Glumboso, that rogue was sent to the galleys, and never had an opportunity to steal any more.

XVIII.

HOW THEY ALL JOURNEYED BACK TO THE CAPITAL.

THE Fairy Blackstick, by whose means this young King and Queen had certainly won their respective crowns back, would come not unfrequently, to pay them a little visit—as they were riding in their triumphal progress towards Giglio's capital—change her wand into a pony, and travel by their Majesties' side, giving them the very best advice. I am not sure that King Giglio did not think the Fairy and her advice rather a bore, fancying it was his own valour and merits which had put him on his throne, and conquered Padella: and, in fine, I fear he rather gave himself airs towards his best friend and patroness. She exhorted him to deal justly by his subjects, to draw mildly on the taxes, never to break his promise when he had once given it—and in all respects to be a good King.

"A good King, my dear Fairy!" cries Rosalba. "Of course he will. Break his promise! can you fancy my Giglio would ever do anything so improper, so unlike him? No! never!" And she looked fondly towards Giglio, whom she thought a pattern of perfection.

"Why is Fairy Blackstick always advising me, and telling me how to manage my government, and warning me to keep my word? Does she suppose that I am not a man of sense, and a man of honour?" asks Giglio, testily. "Methinks she rather presumes upon her position."

"Hush! dear Giglio," says Rosalba. "You know Blackstick has been very kind to us, and we must not offend her." But the Fairy was not listening to Giglio's testy observations, she had fallen back, and was trotting on her pony now, by Master Bulbo's side—who rode a donkey, and made himself generally beloved in the army by his cheerfulness, kindness, and good-humour to everybody. He was eager to see his darling Angelica. He thought there never was such

a charming being. Blackstick did not tell him it was the possession of the magic rose that made Angelica so lovely in his eyes. She brought him the very best accounts of his little wife, whose misfortunes and humiliations had indeed very greatly improved her; and you see, she could whisk off on her wand a hundred miles in a minute, and be back in no time, and so carry polite messages from Bulbo to Angelica, and from Angelica to Bulbo, and comfort that young man upon his journey.

When the Royal party arrived at the last stage before you reach Blombodinga, who should be in waiting, in her carriage there with her lady of honour by her side, but the Princess Angelica. She rushed into her husband's arms, scarcely stopping to make a passing curtsey to the King and Queen. She had no eyes but for Bulbo, who appeared perfectly lovely to her on account of the fairy ring which he wore; whilst she herself, wearing the magic rose in her bonnet, seemed entirely beautiful to the enraptured Bulbo.

A splendid luncheon was served to the Royal party, of which the Archbishop, the Chancellor, the Duke Hedzoff, Countess Gruffanuff, and all our friends partook. The Fairy Blackstick being seated on the left of King Giglio, with Bulbo and Angelica beside. You could hear the joy-bells ringing in the capital, and the guns which the citizens were firing off in honour of their Majesties.

"What can have induced that hideous old Gruffanuff to dress herself up in such an absurd way? Did you ask her to be your bridesmaid, my dear?" says Giglio to Rosalba. "What a figure of fun Gruffy is!"

Gruffy was seated opposite their Majesties, between the Archbishop and the Lord Chancellor, and a figure of fun she certainly was, for she was dressed in a low white silk dress, with lace over, a wreath of white roses on her wig, a splendid lace veil, and her yellow old neck was covered with diamonds. She ogled the King in such a manner, that his Majesty burst out laughing.

"Eleven o'clock!" cries Giglio, as the great Cathedral bell of Blombodinga tolled that hour. "Gentlemen and ladies, we must be starting. Archbishop, you must be at church I think before twelve?"

"We must be at church before twelve," sighs out Gruffanuff in a languishing voice, hiding her old face behind her fan.

"And then I shall be the happiest man in my dominions," cries Giglio, with an elegant bow to the blushing Rosalba.

"O, my Giglio! O, my dear Majesty!" exclaims Gruffanuff; "and can it be that this happy moment at length has arrived—"

"Of course it has arrived," says the King.

—"And that I am about to become the enraptured bride of my adored Giglio!" continues Gruffanuff. "Lend me a smelling-bottle, somebody. I certainly shall faint with joy."

" *You* my bride ? " roars out Giglio.

" *You* marry my Prince ? " cries poor little Rosalba.

" Pooh ! Nonsense ! The woman's mad ! " exclaims the King. And all the courtiers exhibited by their countenances and expressions, marks of surprise, or ridicule, or incredulity, or wonder.

" I should like to know who else is going to be married, if I am not ? " shrieks out Gruffanuff. " I should like to know if King Giglio is a gentleman, and if there is such a thing as justice in Paflagonia ? Lord Chancellor ! my Lord Archbishop ! will your Lordships sit by and see a poor, fond, confiding, tender creature put upon ? Has not Prince Giglio promised to marry his Barbara ? Is not this Giglio's signature ? Does not this paper declare that he is mine, and only mine ? " And she handed to his Grace the Archbishop the document which the Prince signed that evening when she wore the magic ring, and Giglio drank so much champagne. And the old Archbishop, taking out his eye-glasses, read—

" ' *This is to give notice, that I, Giglio, only son of Savio, King of Paflagonia, hereby promise to marry the charming Barbara Griselda Countess Gruffanuff, and widow of the late Jenkins Gruffanuff, Esq.* ' "

" H'm," says the Archbishop, " the document is certainly a—a document."

" Phoo ! " says the Lord Chancellor, " the signature is not in his Majesty's handwriting."

Indeed, since his studies at Bosforo, Giglio had made an immense improvement in caligraphy.

" Is it your handwriting, Giglio ? " cries the Fairy Blackstick, with an awful severity of countenance.

" Y—y—y—es," poor Giglio gasps out, " I had quite forgotten the confounded paper : she can't mean to hold me by it. You old wretch, what will you take to let me off ? Help the Queen, some one —her Majesty has fainted."

" Chop her head off ! "   ) exclaim the impetuous Hedzoff,
" Smother the old witch ! "   } the ardent Smith, and the faithful
" Pitch her into the river ! "   ) Jones.

But Gruffanuff flung her arms round the Archbishop's neck, and bellowed out, " Justice, justice, my Lord Chancellor ! " so loudly, that her piercing shrieks caused everybody to pause. As for Rosalba, she was borne away lifeless by her ladies ; and you may imagine the look of agony which Giglio cast towards that lovely being, as his hope, his joy, his darling, his all in all, was thus removed, and in her place the horrid old Gruffanuff rushed up to his side, and once more shrieked out, " Justice, justice ! "

" Won't you take that sum of money which Glumboso hid ? " says Giglio : " two hundred and eighteen thousand millions, or thereabouts. It's a handsome sum."

" I will have that and you too ! " says Gruffanuff.

" Let us throw the crown jewels into the bargain," gasps out Giglio.

" I will wear them by my Giglio's side ! " says Gruffanuff.

" Will half, three-quarters, five-sixths, nineteen-twentieths, of my kingdom do, Countess ? " asks the trembling monarch.

" What were all Europe to me without *you*, my Giglio ? " cries Gruff, kissing his hand.

" I won't, I can't, I sha'n't,—I'll resign the crown first," shouts Giglio, tearing away his hand; but Gruff clung to it.

" I have a competency, my love," she says, " and with thee and a cottage thy Barbara will be happy."

Giglio was half mad with rage by this time. " I will not marry her," says he. " Oh, Fairy, Fairy, give me counsel ! " And as he spoke he looked wildly round at the severe face of the Fairy Blackstick.

" ' Why is Fairy Blackstick always advising me, and warning me to keep my word? Does she suppose that I am not a man of honour ?' " said the Fairy, quoting Giglio's own haughty words. He quailed under the brightness of her eyes ; he felt that there was no escape for him from that awful inquisition.

" Well, Archbishop," said he, in a dreadful voice that made his Grace start, " since this Fairy has led me to the height of happiness but to dash me down into the depths of despair, since I am to lose Rosalba, let me at least keep my honour. Get up, Countess, and let us be married ; I can keep my word, but I can die afterwards."

" O dear Giglio," cries Gruffanuff, skipping up, " I knew, I knew I could trust thee—I knew that my prince was the soul of honour. Jump into your carriages, ladies and gentlemen, and let us go to church at once ; and as for dying, dear Giglio, no, no :—thou wilt forget that insignificant little chambermaid of a queen—thou wilt live to be consoled by thy Barbara ! She wishes to be a Queen, and not a Queen Dowager, my gracious Lord ! " And hanging upon poor Giglio's arm, and leering and grinning in his face in the most disgusting manner, this old wretch tripped off in her white satin shoes, and jumped into the very carriage which had been got ready to convey Giglio and Rosalba to church. The cannons roared again, the bells pealed triple-bobmajors, the people came out flinging flowers upon the path of the royal bride and bridegroom, and Gruff looked out of the gilt coach window and bowed and grinned to them. Phoo! the horrid old wretch!

XIX.

AND NOW WE COME TO THE LAST SCENE IN THE PANTOMIME.

THE many ups and downs of her life had given the Princess Rosalba prodigious strength of mind, and that highly principled young woman presently recovered from her fainting-fit, out of which Fairy Blackstick, by a precious essence which the Fairy always carried in her pocket, awakened her.

Instead of tearing her hair, crying, and bemoaning herself, and fainting again, as many young women would have done, Rosalba remembered that she owed an example of firmness to her subjects ; and though she loved Giglio more than her life, was determined, as she told the Fairy, not to interfere between him and justice, or to cause him to break his royal word.

"I cannot marry him, but I shall love him always," says she to Blackstick ; " I will go and be present at his marriage with the Countess, and sign the book, and wish them happy with all my heart. I will see, when I get home, whether I cannot make the new Queen some handsome presents. The Crim Tartary crown diamonds are uncommonly fine, and I shall never have any use for them. I will live and die unmarried like Queen Elizabeth, and, of course, I shall leave my crown to Giglio when I quit this world. Let us go and see them married, my dear Fairy, let me say one last farewell to him ; and then, if you please, I will return to my own dominions."

So the Fairy kissed Rosalba with peculiar tenderness, and at once changed her wand into a very comfortable coach-and-four, with a steady coachman, and two respectable footmen behind, and the Fairy and Rosalba got into the coach, which Angelica and Bulbo entered after them.

As for honest Bulbo, he was blubbering in the most pathetic manner, quite overcome by Rosalba's misfortune. She was touched by the honest fellow's sympathy, promised to restore to him the confiscated estates of Duke Padella his father, and created him, as he sat there in the coach, Prince, Highness, and First Grandee of the Crim Tartar Empire.

The coach moved on, and, being a fairy coach, soon came up with the bridal procession.

Before the ceremony at church it was the custom in Paflagonia, as it is in other countries, for the bride and bridegroom to sign the Contract of Marriage, which was to be witnessed by the Chancellor, Minister, Lord Mayor, and principal officers of state.

Now, as the royal palace was being painted and furnished anew, it was not ready for the reception of the King and his bride, who proposed at first to take up their residence at the Prince's palace, that one which Valoroso occupied when Angelica was born, and before he usurped the throne.

So the marriage party drove up to the palace : the dignitaries got out of their carriages and stood aside : poor Rosalba stepped out of her coach, supported by Bulbo, and stood almost fainting up against the railings so as to have a last look of her dear Giglio.

As for Blackstick, she, according to her custom, had flown out of the coach window in some inscrutable manner, and was now standing at the palace door.

Giglio came up the steps with his horrible bride on his arm, looking as pale as if he was going to execution. He only frowned at the Fairy Blackstick—he was angry with her, and thought she came to insult his misery.

"Get out of the way, pray," says Gruffanuff, haughtily. "I wonder why you are always poking your nose into other people's affairs?"

"Are you determined to make this poor young man unhappy?" says Blackstick.

"To marry him, yes! What business is it of yours? Pray, madam, don't say 'you' to a Queen," cries Gruffanuff.

MADAM GRUFFANUFF FINDS A HUSBAND.

"You won't take the money he offered you?"

"No."

"You won't let him off his bargain, though you know you cheated him when you made him sign the paper?"

"Impudence! Policemen, remove this woman!" cries Gruff-anuff. And the policemen were rushing forward, but with a wave of her wand the Fairy struck them all like so many statues in their places.

"You won't take anything in exchange for your bond, Mrs. Gruff-anuff," cries the Fairy, with awful severity. "I speak for the last time."

"No!" shrieks Gruffanuff, stamping with her foot. "I'll have my husband, my husband, my husband!"

"You SHALL HAVE YOUR HUSBAND!" the Fairy Blackstick cried; and advancing a step, laid her hand upon the nose of the KNOCKER.

As she touched it, the brass nose seemed to elongate, the open mouth opened still wider, and uttered a roar which made everybody start. The eyes rolled wildly; the arms and legs uncurled themselves, writhed about, and seemed to lengthen with each twist; the knocker expanded into a figure in yellow livery, six feet high; the screws by which it was fixed to the door unloosed themselves, and JENKINS GRUFFANUFF once more trod the threshold off which he had been lifted more than twenty years ago!

"Master's not at home," says Jenkins, just in his old voice; and Mrs. Jenkins, giving a dreadful *youp*, fell down in a fit, in which nobody minded her.

For everybody was shouting, "Huzzay! huzzay!" "Hip, hip, hurray!" "Long live the King and Queen!" "Were such things ever seen?" "No, never, never, never!" "The Fairy Blackstick for ever!"

The bells were ringing double peals, the guns roaring and banging most prodigiously.

Bulbo was embracing everybody; the Lord Chancellor was fling-ing up his wig and shouting like a madman; Hedzoff had got the Archbishop round the waist, and they were dancing a jig for joy; and as for Giglio, I leave you to imagine what *he* was doing, and if he kissed Rosalba once, twice—twenty thousand times, I'm sure I don't think he was wrong.

So Gruffanuff opened the hall door with a low bow, just as he had been accustomed to do, and they all went in and signed the book, and then they went to church and were married, and the Fairy Blackstick sailed away on her cane, and was never more heard of in Paflagonia.

AND HERE ENDS THE FIRE-SIDE PANTOMIME.

LONDON: PRINTED BY
SPOTTISWOODE AND CO., NEW-STREET SQUARE
AND PARLIAMENT STREET

W. M. THACKERAY'S WORKS.

NEW 'STANDARD' EDITION. To be completed in 26 vols.
large 8vo. 10s. 6d. each. This Edition will contain some of Mr. Thackeray's
writings not before collected, with many additional Illustrations. Several
Volumes have already been issued, and a Volume will be published on the 1st
of each succeeding month until the conclusion of the Series.

THE ÉDITION DE LUXE. Twenty-four Volumes, imperial
8vo. Containing 248 Steel Engravings, 1,473 Wood Engravings, and 88 Coloured
Illustrations. The steel and wood engravings are all printed on real China
paper. The NUMBER of COPIES PRINTED is LIMITED to ONE THOU-
SAND, each copy being numbered. The Work can only be obtained through
Booksellers, who will furnish information regarding terms, &c.

THE LIBRARY EDITION. With Illustrations by the Author,
RICHARD DOYLE, and FREDERICK WALKER. Twenty-two Volumes, large
crown 8vo. handsomely bound in cloth, price £8. 5s.; or half-russia, marbled
edges, £12. 12s.
     *** The Volumes are sold separately, in cloth, price 7s. 6d. each.*

THE POPULAR EDITION. 12 vols. crown 8vo. with Frontispiece
to each volume, scarlet cloth, gilt top, price £3; and in half-morocco,
price £5. 5s.
     *** The Volumes are sold separately, in green cloth, price 5s. each.*

CHEAPER ILLUSTRATED EDITION. In Twenty-four Volumes,
crown 8vo. price 3s. 6d. each. In Sets of Twenty-four Volumes uniformly
bound in cloth, price £4. 4s.; or handsomely bound in half-morocco, price £8.
Containing nearly all the small Woodcut Illustrations of the former Editions
and many New Illustrations by Eminent Artists.

THIS EDITION CONTAINS ALTOGETHER 1,626 ILLUSTRATIONS

By the AUTHOR; LUKE FILDES, A.R.A.; Mrs. BUTLER (Miss Elizabeth Thompson);
GEORGE DU MAURIER; RICHARD DOYLE; FREDERICK WALKER, A.R.A.; GEORGE
CRUIKSHANK; JOHN LEECH; FRANK DICKSEE; LINLEY SAMBOURNE; F. BARNARD;
E. J. WHEELER; F. A. FRASER; CHARLES KEENE; R. B. WALLACE; J. P.
ATKINSON; W. J. WEBB; T. R. MACQUOID; M. FITZGERALD; W. RALSTON;
JOHN COLLIER; H. FURNISS; G. G. KILBURNE, &c., &c., &c.

BALLADS. By WILLIAM MAKEPEACE THACKERAY. With a Por-
trait of the Author, and 56 Illustrations by the Author; Mrs. BUTLER (Miss
Elizabeth Thompson); GEORGE DU MAURIER; JOHN COLLIER; H. FURNISS;
G. G. KILBURNE; M. FITZGERALD; and J. P. ATKINSON. Printed on toned
paper by Clay, Sons, & Taylor; and elegantly bound in cloth, gilt edges, by
Burn. Small 4to. 16s.

W. M. THACKERAY'S SKETCHES.

THE ORPHAN OF PIMLICO, and other Sketches, Frag-
ments, and Drawings. By WILLIAM MAKEPEACE THACKERAY. Copied by
a process that gives a faithful reproduction of the originals. With a Preface
and Editorial Notes by Miss Thackeray. A New Edition, in a new style
of binding, bevelled boards, gilt edges, royal 4to. price One Guinea.

London: SMITH, ELDER, & CO., 15 Waterloo Place.